W9-DEG-802

Illustrated Classics From India

Over 86 million copies of over 400 titles sold worldwide!

Amar Chitra Katha is a collection of illustrated classics that retell stories from Indian mythology, history, folktale and legend through the fascinating medium of comics. Over 430 stories from all over India have been told in this series that has been endorsed by educationists and recommended by teachers the world over.

Through a masterful blend of commentary, dialogue and illustration, Amar Chitra Katha presents complex historical facts and intricate mythology in a format that would appeal to children. They not only entertain, but also provide a fitting introduction to the cultural heritage of India. In a country so vast and varied, the series also serves as a medium for national integration, by introducing young readers to the rich cultural diversity of the country and highlighting the achievements of local heroes.

Amar Chitra Katha comics are like family heirlooms, passed down from generation to generation. These timeless illustrated classics are now also available online on www. AmarChitraKatha.com. Start your own collection today!

No.1004 • Rs 195

INDIA BOOK HOUSE

© India Book House Pvt. Ltd. 1998   Reprinted: December 2006   ISBN: 81-7508-145-7
Published and Printed by India Book House Pvt Ltd, Mahalaxmi Chambers,
5th Floor, 22 Bhulabhai Desai Road, Mumbai 400 026, India.

AMAR CHITRA KATHA

Illustrated Classics From India

Panchatantra
The Jackal and the Wardrum

The original text of the Panchatantra in Sanskrit was written about 200 BC by a great Hindi scholar, Pandit Vishnu Sharma. Some of the tales themselves must be much older, their origin going back to the period of the Vedas and the Upanishads (1500 BC to 500 BC). In course of time, travellers carried these stories to Persia and Arabia and finally, through Greece, to Europe.

The Panchatantra has been translated into over 50 languages. It teaches us how to understand people, how to choose reliable and trustworthy friends, how to meet difficulties and solve problems through tact and wisdom and how to live in peace and harmony in the face of hypocrisy, deceit and the many pitfalls in life. Difficult subjects like philosophy, psychology, politics, music, astronomy, and human relations are discussed in a simple but lyrical style.

Script: G.L. Chandiramani   Illustrations: Jeffrey Fowler   Cover: Jeffrey Fowler

THE JACKAL AND THE WAR DRUM.

GOMAYA THE JACKAL HAD NOT EATEN FOR MANY DAYS AND WAS VERY HUNGRY.

IF I DON'T FIND SOME FOOD SOON, I WILL DIE.

AS HE WANDERED THROUGH THE FOREST IN SEARCH OF FOOD HE CAME UPON AN OLD BATTLEFIELD.

WHAT'S THAT NOISE? I'D BETTER RUN BEFORE I'M ATTACKED.

WHIR WHOOSH

WHIR! WHOOSH!

ZOOM

NO! I WON'T RUN. I'LL BE BRAVE AND FIND OUT WHO'S MAKING THE NOISE.

SCREEEECH

SO HE CREPT BACK TRYING TO BE BRAVE.

WHIR! WHOOSH

TO HIS ASTONISHMENT GOMAYA FOUND THAT THE NOISE CAME FROM A HARMLESS OLD WAR DRUM.

WHIR! WHOOSH!

THE LOW BRANCHES OF A TREE WERE SWISHING AGAINST IT AND MAKING THE NOISE. NEAR THE DRUM THERE WAS PLENTY OF FOOD.

WHIR! WHOOSH!

WHIR! WHOOSH!

WHAT A FOOL I'D HAVE BEEN IF I'D LET A SILLY OLD WAR DRUM CHEAT ME OF ALL THIS DELICIOUS FOOD!

MORALS: FEAR OF THE UNKNOWN BRINGS NO GAIN.

THE COBRA AND THE CROW.

ONCE, THERE LIVED A PAIR OF CROWS ON AN OLD TREE. IN THE HOLLOW OF THE SAME TREE THERE LIVED A WICKED COBRA.

EVERY TIME I LAY EGGS, THIS WICKED COBRA EATS THEM ALL UP. WHAT SHALL WE DO?

LET'S ASK OUR FRIEND, THE JACKAL. HE'S A CLEVER FELLOW.

SAY FRIEND, THERE'S A BAD OLD COBRA WHO LIVES IN OUR TREE. HE EATS ALL OUR CHILDREN. HOW CAN WE GET RID OF HIM AND PROTECT OUR HOME?

J.JACKAL

THE JACKAL THOUGHT FOR A WHILE.

THEN —

I'LL TELL YOU HOW. LISTEN TO ME CAREFULLY. B..z..z..z....

ACCORDING TO PLAN, THE CROWS FLEW OVER A LAKE WHERE THE QUEEN AND HER MAIDS WERE BATHING. THEY HAD LEFT THEIR CLOTHES AND JEWELRY ON THE BANK OF THE LAKE.

NOW YOU KNOW WHAT TO DO.

THE FEMALE CROW SWOOPED DOWN, PICKED UP A GOLD NECKLACE AND FLEW OFF.

FLAP!

FLAP!

SOME OF THE KING'S SERVANTS, WHO WERE WORKING NEARBY, HEARD THE WOMEN SHOUTING. THEY BEGAN CHASING THE CROW.

SHE FLEW OVER THE HOME OF THE BAD COBRA AND DROPPED THE NECKLACE NEARBY.

A COBRA.

THE COBRA CAME OUT...

?

... AND THE ANGRY SERVANTS SAW HIM.

Kill him! KILL HIM!

BAM

THUD

THAT WAS THE END OF THE WICKED OLD COBRA.

THE MEN GOT BACK THE GOLD CHAIN AND THE CROWS LIVED HAPPILY EVER AFTER.

MORAL : MIGHTY BRAWN IS NO MATCH FOR NIMBLE BRAIN.

THE TURTLE WHO FELL OFF A STICK.

NEAR A CERTAIN LAKE THERE LIVED A TURTLE AND TWO SWANS. THEY SPENT MOST OF THEIR TIME IN TELLING EACH OTHER STORIES.

AND SO IT CAME TO PASS...

SO THE YEARS PASSED. THEN SUDDENLY ONE YEAR THERE WAS A DROUGHT.

THE LAKE IS ALMOST DRY. HOW CAN WE LIVE WITHOUT WATER?

DON'T WORRY. WE WILL FIND A WAY OUT.

SUDDENLY THE TURTLE HAD AN IDEA.

FIRST FIND A LAKE FULL OF WATER. THEN BRING ME A STICK. I'LL HOLD ON TO THE MIDDLE OF IT. YOU HOLD THE ENDS AND CARRY ME TO OUR NEW LAKE.

GOOD, BUT WHILE WE ARE FLYING, TAKE CARE THAT YOU DON'T OPEN YOUR MOUTH.

THE SWANS FOUND THE LAKE AND CAME BACK TO THE TURTLE WITH A STICK.

OKAY. GET READY! HERE WE GO.

CAN YOU SEE THAT TOWN THERE? WE'LL SOON HAVE TO FLY OVER IT.

AS THEY FLEW OVER THE TOWN —

LOOK... LOOK AT THOSE CLEVER BIRDS. THEY'RE CARRYING SOMETHING, IT'S A TURTLE!

WHAT IS ALL THAT EXCITEMENT ABOUT? ME?

ALAS THE TURTLE HAD FORGOTTEN TO KEEP HER MOUTH SHUT. SHE FELL DOWN ---

--- AND DIED.

BASH

WHAT LUCK! LET'S COOK IT FOR DINNER TONIGHT. TURTLE MEAT TASTES DELICIOUS.

MORAL : SILENCE IS GOLDEN.

THE MONKEY AND THE LOG.

ONCE, CERTAIN WORKMEN WERE BUSY BUILDING A TEMPLE ON THE OUTSKIRTS OF A TOWN.

WHEN IT WAS NOON —

LET US GO TO THE TOWN FOR LUNCH.

I'LL JUST PUT A WEDGE HERE AND COME.

I HOPE NO ONE TOUCHES THAT WEDGE WHILE WE ARE AWAY.

HARDLY HAD THE WORKMEN LEFT, WHEN A GROUP OF MONKEYS ARRIVED ON THE SCENE.

ONE OF THEM PERCHED HIMSELF ON THE HALF-SAWN LOG.

WHAT IS THIS PIECE OF WOOD DOING HERE?

I WONDER WHAT WILL HAPPEN IF I PULL IT OUT?

SO HE PULLED AT THE WEDGE.

UGH! IT'S TOUGH.

OUT IT CAME.

HELP

THE GAP CLOSED IN, TRAPPING THE MONKEY'S LEG.

SNAP

THE POOR MONKEY WAS INSTANTLY KILLED.

MORAL : DO NOT MEDDLE WITH THINGS THAT DO NOT CONCERN YOU.

A MERCHANT AND A KING'S SERVANT.

ONCE UPON A TIME, IN A CITY CALLED VARDHAMANA —

HE IS WISE AND GOOD TOO!

ONCE AGAIN DANTILA HAS PROVED HIMSELF TO BE AN EXCELLENT ADMINISTRATOR.

WHILE THE PEOPLE WERE PRAISING HIM, DANTILA WAS BUSY TALKING WITH HIS WIFE ABOUT THEIR DAUGHTER'S WEDDING.

I HAVE INVITED THE KING, THE QUEEN, AND THE ENTIRE COURT FOR THE WEDDING.

WE'D BETTER START THE PREPARATIONS. THERE ARE HARDLY A FEW DAYS LEFT.

ON THE WEDDING DAY —

WELCOME, O KING. I AM HIGHLY HONOURED BY YOUR PRESENCE TODAY.

GORAMBA THE KING'S SWEEPER CAME TO THE WEDDING, TOO, BUT UNINVITED.

DANTILA WAS FURIOUS.

GET OUT, GORAMBA! HOW DARE YOU COME HERE?

I'LL GET EVEN WITH HIM SOMEHOW.

THE WHOLE OF THAT NIGHT HE THOUGHT ABOUT IT.

AT LAST JUST BEFORE SUNRISE —

I'VE GOT IT!

THAT MORNING WHEN GORAMBA WENT TO SWEEP THE KING'S CHAMBER —

SHAME ON DANTILA! HOW DARE HE EMBRACE THE QUEEN!

GORAMBA, WHAT WERE YOU SAYING? TELL ME AT ONCE, IS IT TRUE?

MASTER! PLEASE! I WAS GAMBLING ALL NIGHT. NOW I'M HALF ASLEEP AND I DON'T KNOW WHAT I'M SAYING.

GORAMBA MOVES FREELY IN THE PALACE. MAYBE HE REALLY SAW IT HAPPEN.

THE KING DRESSED AND SENT FOR HIS CHIEF GUARD.

HENCEFORTH, DANTILA SHALL NOT ENTER THE PALACE GATES.

YES, YOUR MAJESTY.

THE NEXT DAY DANTILA WANTED TO MEET THE KING. BUT —

WHY.. B..BUT... I-I-I...

HA! HA! HA!

SORRY YOU MAY NOT ENTER. THE KING'S ORDERS.

NOW I KNOW WHO CAUSED THE TROUBLE! A KING'S SERVANT HIGH OR LOW, MUST INDEED BE RESPECTED.

THAT VERY EVENING DANTILA INVITED GORAMBA TO HIS HOME.

MY FRIEND, PLEASE ACCEPT THESE GIFTS AND FORGIVE ME FOR MY BEHAVIOUR THAT DAY.

THANK YOU SIR, THANK YOU.

I FORGIVE YOU. AND YOU WILL SEE AGAIN HOW CLEVER I CAN BE.

THE NEXT MORNING GORAMBA WAS SWEEPING THE KING'S ROOM AS USUAL.

HO! HO! HA! HA! OUR KING EATS CUCUMBERS IN THE LAVATORY.

THAT'S A LIE, GORAMBA. I COULD HANG YOU FOR IT.

P..P..PLEASE! M-MA-MASTER! I WAS GAMBLING ALL NIGHT. NOW I'M HALF ASLEEP. I DON'T KNOW WHAT I'M SAYING. PLEASE FORGIVE ME!

HE HAS MADE A MISTAKE ABOUT ME. SO HE COULD BE WRONG ABOUT DANTILA TOO. I MUST MAKE UP WITH THE ABLE DANTILA.

DANTILA, MY DEAR FRIEND, ACCEPT THESE GIFTS AS A TOKEN OF MY REGARD FOR YOU. YOU ARE REAPPOINTED TO YOUR FORMER POSITION AND MAY ENTER THE PALACE AT WILL!

THANK YOU, YOUR MAJESTY.

MORAL : EVERY DOG HAS ITS DAY.

THE MERCHANT'S SON AND THE IRON BALANCE.

IN A CERTAIN TOWN, THERE LIVED A MERCHANT CALLED JWEERNADHANA.

I HAVE LOST ALL MY MONEY IN BUSINESS HERE. LET ME TRY MY LUCK IN SOME OTHER TOWN.

BEFORE LEAVING HE VISITED ANOTHER MERCHANT, A FRIEND.

FRIEND, WILL YOU KEEP THIS IRON BALANCE FOR ME TILL I RETURN?

I WILL!

JWEERNADHANA SET OUT ON HIS JOURNEY.

I HOPE I COME BACK RICH!

AFTER A FEW MONTHS JWEERNADHANA RETURNED AND WENT TO MEET HIS FRIEND.

FRIEND, I HAVE COME FOR MY BALANCE.

I'M SORRY. THE RATS ATE IT UP.

JWEERNADHANA KNEW THAT HIS FRIEND WAS LYING. BUT WHAT COULD HE DO?

THEN SUDDENLY HE HAD AN IDEA.

WELL! FRIEND. I CAN'T BLAME YOU. ANYWAY I'LL GO FOR A BATH. CAN YOU SEND YOUR LITTLE SON WITH ME TO HELP ME CARRY MY BELONGINGS?

SURE. WHY NOT!

SO THE LITTLE BOY ACCOMPANIED JWEERNADHANA AND CARRIED HIS BELONGINGS FOR HIM.

ON THE WAY THEY CAME UPON A CAVE.

LET'S ENTER IT AND SEE WHAT IT'S LIKE INSIDE.

ONCE INSIDE, JWEERNADHANA LEFT THE BOY AND QUICKLY RAN OUT.

THEN HE BLOCKED THE ENTRANCE WITH A HUGE BOULDER.

WELL! NOW THE BOY CAN'T COME OUT.

THEN HE RETURNED TO HIS FRIEND.

WHY ARE YOU ALONE? WHERE IS MY LITTLE SON?

I'M SORRY, FRIEND. A FLAMINGO PICKED HIM UP AND FLEW OFF.

WHAT! YOU LIAR! HOW COULD THAT BE? BRING BACK MY SON OR I'LL TAKE YOU TO THE JUDGE.

LET'S GO. I'M NOT AFRAID!

SO THEY WENT TO THE JUDGE.

JUDGE, THIS ROGUE HAS KIDNAPPED MY ONLY SON. I WANT JUSTICE.

JUDGE

JWEERNADHANA, I COMMAND YOU TO RETURN HIS SON TO HIM.

I'M SORRY, JUDGE. BUT I CAN'T. A FLAMINGO FLEW OFF WITH HIM.

YOU ARE LYING, JWEERNADHANA. BE CAREFUL.

AM I? WELL IF RATS CAN EAT AN IRON BALANCE, WHY CAN'T A FLAMINGO FLY OFF WITH A CHILD?

WHAT ARE YOU TRYING TO SAY? PLEASE EXPLAIN YOURSELF.

WHEN JWEERNADHANA EXPLAINED EVERYTHING—

HA HA HA HO HO HA SHAHEE

—HEY, YOU THERE! RETURN THE IRON BALANCE TO HIM AND JWEERNADHANA WILL RETURN YOUR SON TO YOU.

MORAL: **TIT FOR TAT.**

THE JACKAL WHO FELL INTO A VAT OF INDIGO DYE.

ONCE A JACKAL GOT SO HUNGRY THAT HE VENTURED INTO A TOWN IN SEARCH OF FOOD.

THE TOWN DOGS ARE AFTER ME! HELP!

DYERS

TO SAVE HIMSELF FROM THE DOGS HE RAN INTO A DYER'S YARD AND...

... FELL INTO A VAT OF INDIGO DYE.

EYEO GLUB!

WHEN HE CAME OUT THE DOGS COULD NOT RECOGNISE HIM. THEY RAN AWAY IN PANIC.

I SHALL GO BACK TO THE JUNGLE.

BACK IN THE JUNGLE THE OTHER ANIMALS TOO WERE FRIGHTENED.

I MUST THINK FAST.

DON'T RUN AWAY. LORD BRAHMA HAS CROWNED ME YOUR NEW KING. COME BACK. I WILL PROTECT ALL OF YOU.

THUS ASSURED, THE ANIMALS RETURNED · THEN —

CHASE ALL THESE DIRTY JACKALS AWAY · I SHALL HAVE NOTHING TO DO WITH THEM ·

THAT NIGHT WHEN THE JUNGLE WAS ABSOLUTELY STILL, THE JACKALS BEGAN HOWLING.

TRUE TO HIS NATURE THE BLUE JACKAL BEGAN HOWLING ALONG WITH HIS BROTHERS.

WOOOOOOOO WOOOOOOOO

HEY! OUR KING IS ONLY A JACKAL · WE HAVE BEEN FOOLED · HE SHALL DIE FOR THIS ·

WOOOOOO

SO THEY POUNCED ON THE BLUE JACKAL AND...

... THAT WAS THE END OF HIM ·

MORAL : A COAT OF PAINT CANNOT HIDE ONE'S TRUE COLOURS ·

THE HERON AND THE CRAB.

AN OLD HERON LIVED IN A JUNGLE NEAR A BIG LAKE WHICH WAS FULL OF FISHES, CRABS AND OTHER WATER CREATURES.

I AM SO OLD AND FEEBLE, I CAN HARDLY CATCH ANY FISH. UNLESS I FIND A WAY OUT, I WILL SOON DIE.

ONE DAY HE SAT AT THE EDGE OF THE LAKE AND BEGAN CRYING. A CRAB CAME TO HIM.

UNCLE, WHAT'S THE MATTER? WHY ARE YOU CRYING? AREN'T YOU GOING TO EAT ANY FISH TODAY?

FROM TODAY I SHALL FAST UNTO DEATH.

BUT WHY?

AN ASTROLOGER TOLD ME THIS MORNING THAT THERE WILL BE NO RAIN FOR 12 YEARS. THE LAKES WILL DRY UP. WE SHALL ALL DIE.

THE CRAB TOLD THIS TO ALL THE OTHER WATER CREATURES. THEY WERE PANIC-STRICKEN.

THEY SENT THE CRAB TO ASK THE HERON WHAT THEY SHOULD DO.

THIS MEANS SURE DEATH FOR US. PLEASE TELL US HOW WE CAN SAVE OURSELVES.

WELL, NOT FAR AWAY THERE IS A BIG LAKE, WHICH WILL NEVER DRY UP. I WILL TAKE YOU THERE, ONE BY ONE.

THE HERON HAD SUCCEEDED IN GAINING THEIR CONFIDENCE.

UNCLE! BROTHER! FATHER ME FIRST! NO ME! PLEASE!

THE WICKED HERON TOOK THEM, ONE BY ONE, TO A ROCK NEARBY AND ATE THEM.

ONE DAY THE CRAB CAME TO THE HERON.

UNCLE, PLEASE SAVE ME TOO! DON'T FORGET I WAS YOUR FRIEND FIRST.

I AM TIRED OF EATING FISH EVERY DAY. CRAB SHOULD BE FINE FOR A CHANGE.

SO THE HERON TOOK THE CRAB.

AH! FISH BONES. NOW I UNDERSTAND ALL!

UNCLE, YOU MUST BE TIRED. AM I TOO HEAVY? WHERE IS THE LAKE?

NOW THIS DUMB CRAB CANNOT ESCAPE ME. I MAY AS WELL TELL HIM THE TRUTH.

O FOOLISH CRAB. THERE IS NO OTHER LAKE. THIS TRIP IS FOR MY FOOD. I WILL SOON DASH YOU AGAINST A ROCK AND EAT YOU.

THE MINUTE, THE HERON SAID THIS, THE CRAB CAUGHT HIS NECK BETWEEN HIS CLAWS AND STRANGLED HIM.

THAT WAS THE END OF THE WICKED OLD HERON.

BONG

THE CRAB GRIPPED THE HERON BY HIS NECK AND DRAGGED HIM SLOWLY TO THE LAKE.

HA! HA! HA! FASTING TO DEATH! POOR FISHES.

WHEN HE REACHED THE LAKE HE WAS STILL LAUGHING.

CRAB, WHY ARE YOU BACK? WHAT HAS HAPPENED TO UNCLE? WE ARE ALL WAITING FOR OUR TURN, TO BE TAKEN TO THE OTHER POND.

YOU FOOLS, HE HAS EATEN ALL YOUR BROTHERS. I FOUND OUT AND KILLED HIM.

MORAL: ONE MAY SMILE AND SMILE AND YET BE A VILLAIN.

DHARMABUDDHI AND PAPABUDDHI.

IN A CERTAIN VILLAGE THERE ONCE LIVED TWO FRIENDS CALLED DHARMABUDDHI AND PAPABUDDHI. PAPABUDDHI WAS A DISHONEST MAN.

IF I CAN GET DHARMABUDDHI TO START SOME BUSINESS WITH ME, I CAN CHEAT HIM OF HIS SHARE AND BECOME A RICH MAN.

SO HE WENT TO DHARMABUDDHI.

FRIEND, I HAVE AN IDEA. LET US GO OUT INTO THE WORLD AND MAKE SOME MONEY.

WHY NOT?

SO THEY SET OFF TOWARDS THE NEAREST TOWN.

THEY SOON MADE A LOT OF MONEY AND WERE ON THEIR WAY BACK HOME. SUDDENLY PAPABUDDHI ASKED HIS FRIEND TO HALT.

A THOUGHT JUST STRUCK ME. IT IS NOT SAFE TO TAKE ALL THE MONEY BACK WITH US. LET US TAKE ONLY A SMALL SUM AND BURY THE REST HERE.

QUITE RIGHT. LET'S.

THERE! NOW WE NEED FEAR NO THIEVES OR BURGLARS.

AND I CAN COME BACK AND COLLECT IT ALL.

THEY SOON REACHED HOME. THAT NIGHT —

I HOPE NO ONE SEES ME. I MUST BE QUICK.

THE NEXT DAY PAPABUDDHI WENT TO DHARMABUDDHI'S HOUSE.

FRIEND, I HAVE FINISHED ALL MY MONEY. LET'S GO AND FETCH SOME MORE.

SPENT IT ALL SO SOON? WELL! LET'S GO.

SO OFF THEY WENT. BUT WHEN THEY DUG UP THE PIT, THE POT OF MONEY WAS NOWHERE TO BE SEEN.

OH! DHARMABUDDHI! YOU CALL YOURSELF MY FRIEND. RETURN THE MONEY OR I'LL TAKE YOU TO THE JUDGE.

I AM AN HONEST MAN. HOW COULD YOU SUSPECT ME? AND **YOU** CALL **YOURSELF** MY FRIEND.

QUARRELLING ALL THE WAY, THEY WENT TO THE JUDGE.

I DIDN'T.

YOU DID.

THIS MAN HAS STOLEN THE MONEY. THE FOREST GOD IS MY WITNESS. HE WILL SPEAK THE TRUTH.

ALL RIGHT. WE WILL GO TO THE FOREST TOMORROW.

PAPABUDDHI WENT STRAIGHT HOME TO HIS FATHER.

FATHER, I HAVE STOLEN DHARMABUDDHI'S MONEY. YOU WILL HAVE TO DO AS I SAY IF I AM TO ESCAPE.

I'LL DO AS YOU WANT ME TO, MY SON.

THE NEXT MORNING DHARMABUDDHI, PAPABUDDHI, THE JUDGE AND THE VILLAGE ELDERS WENT UP TO WHERE THE MONEY HAD BEEN BURIED.

O TREE GOD. TELL US WHO THE THIEF IS!

DHARMABUDDHI IS THE THIEF.

WHILE THE OTHERS WERE BUSY DISCUSSING THE CASE, DHARMABUDDHI WAS BUSY COLLECTING DRIED LEAVES AND TWIGS. THESE HE PLACED NEAR THE HOLLOW OF THE TREE AND ···

··· SET THEM ALIGHT.

AS THE FIRE ROSE INTO THE HOLLOW, OUT RAN PAPABUDDHI'S FATHER.

IT'S ALL MY SON'S FAULT.

PAPABUDDHI'S FATHER. WELL!

THE JUDGE UNDERSTOOD ALL AND WAS ANGRY.

PAPABUDDHI MADE ME DO THIS.

FOR THIS CRIME HE SHALL BE HANGED ON THIS VERY TREE RIGHT NOW.

MORAL: HONESTY IS THE BEST POLICY.

THE LION AND THE HARE.

IN A CERTAIN JUNGLE THERE LIVED A LION CALLED BHASURAKA. HE WAS VERY STRONG AND KILLED THE ANIMALS IN THE JUNGLE JUST FOR FUN.

GRRRR

OH! WHY DOES HE HAVE TO KILL US WHEN HE IS NOT HUNGRY?

ONE DAY ALL THE SURVIVING ANIMALS APPROACHED BHASURAKA.

MASTER, WHY KILL US ALL WHEN ONE OF US WOULD SATISFY YOUR HUNGER? FROM TODAY ONE OF US WILL COME TO YOU EACH DAY. IN RETURN YOU MUST LET THE OTHERS LIVE IN PEACE.

ALL RIGHT. BUT IF YOU FAIL TO COME, I SHALL KILL ALL OF YOU.

EVERY DAY THE ANIMALS DREW LOTS. ONE DAY —

OH! POOR HARE!
IT IS YOUR TURN TODAY.

MOST RELUCTANTLY THE
HARE MADE HIS WAY TO
BHASURAKA.

I WISH I COULD KILL
HIM AND SAVE MY
LIFE!

SUDDENLY HE CAME ACROSS A WELL.
HE WAS JUBILANT.

NOW I KNOW A WAY
TO KILL HIM. AND
I WON'T FAIL.

BY THE TIME THE HARE
REACHED BHASURAKA IT
WAS SUNSET. AND BHASU-
RAKA WAS FURIOUS.

THE FIRST THING
I'LL DO TOMOR-
ROW IS
TO KILL
ALL THE
ANIMALS.

CAUTIOUSLY THE HARE NEARED BHASURAKA.

AS IT IS YOU ARE SMALL.
APART FROM THAT, YOU ARE
LATE. I'LL KILL YOU
NOW AND THE OTHERS
TOMORROW.

HURRY UP, THEN, AND TELL ME. I'M HUNGRY.

MASTER, IT IS NOT MY FAULT. PLEASE LET ME EXPLAIN.

BHASURAKA LION

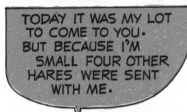

TODAY IT WAS MY LOT TO COME TO YOU. BUT BECAUSE I'M SMALL FOUR OTHER HARES WERE SENT WITH ME.

ON THE WAY WE MET A BIG LION. HE ASKED US WHERE WE WERE GOING. SO WE TOLD HIM WE WERE ON OUR WAY TO OUR MASTER TO KEEP OUR PROMISE.

WHO WAS THIS LION?

I AM THE LORD OF THIS JUNGLE. NOT HE. GO AND CHALLENGE HIM TO FIGHT ME. I SHALL **KILL** HIM.

YES MASTER! BUT HE LIVES IN A STRONGHOLD. IT IS UNWISE TO ATTACK HIM THERE.

SURAKA LION

THE HARE TOOK BHASURAKA TO THE WELL.

THAT IS NOT YOUR CONCERN. JUST SHOW HIM TO ME.

VERY WELL THEN, COME MASTER...

WHEN THEY REACHED THE WELL —

I'LL KILL HIM.

MY LORD, THE RASCAL IS AFRAID. HE IS HIDING IN THE WELL. LOOK!

HE DIVED INTO THE WELL AND...

... WAS DROWNED.

SPLASH

BHASURAKA IS DEAD. I AM SAFE.

THE END

MORAL : NOTHING IS IMPOSSIBLE FOR A CLEVER MAN.

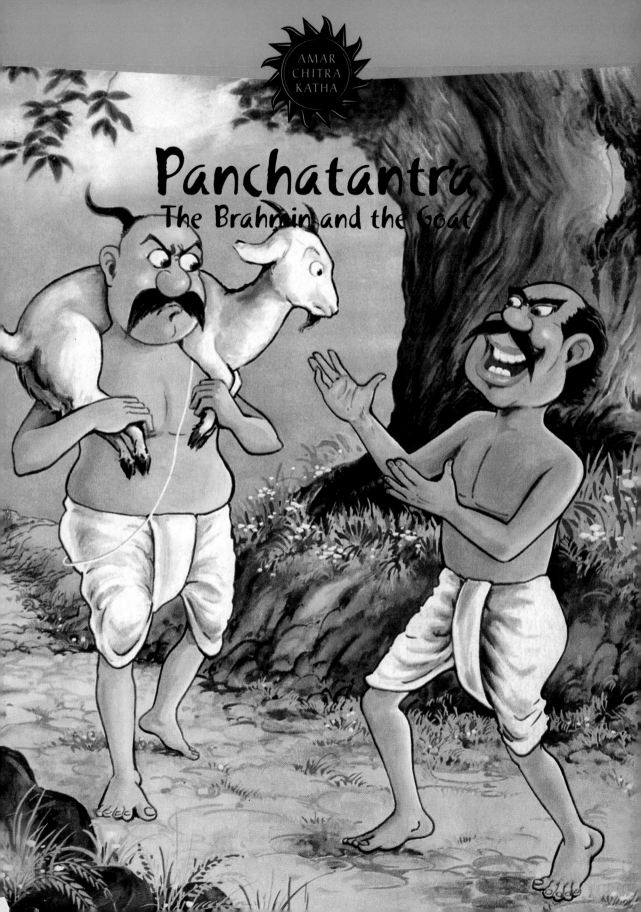

Panchatantra
The Brahmin and the Goat

Illustrated Classics From India

Panchatantra
The Brahmin and the Goat and other Stories

The original text of the Panchatantra in Sanskrit was probably written about 200 B.C. by a great Hindi scholar, Pandit Vishnu Sharma. Some of the tales themselves must be much older, their origin going back to the period of the Vedas and the Upanishads (1500 B.C. to 500 B.C.). In the course of time, travellers took these stories with them to Persia and Arabia and finally, through Greece, they reached Europe. So far the Panchatantra has been translated into more than 50 languages of the world.

How the tales of the Panchatantra came to be told is in itself an interesting story. A king in ancient India could not find a teacher who could make his three sons interested in the pursuit of knowledge. At last he found in Pandit Vishnu Sharma the teacher he was looking for.

The theories of philosophy, psychology and statecraft became engrossing when Vishnu Sharma drove their moral lessons home through stories of talking animals and their escapades.

One unique feature of the tales is that most of the characters are animals; another is that the tales form a chain of stories; third, each of the tales has a distinct moral; and yet another, the tales have different levels of appeal.

The morals that the Panchatantra seeks to teach continue to be relevant to this day and the stories themselves still retain their novelty even two thousand years after they were first told.

Script: Shyamala Kutty   Illustrations: Ashok Dongre   Cover: Ashok Dongre

THE BRAHMAN AND THE GOAT

ONE DAY, A BRAHMAN CALLED MITRA SHARMA WAS RETURNING HOME FROM A NEIGHBOURING VILLAGE.

IT WAS KIND OF THAT VILLAGER TO GIVE ME THIS PLUMP GOAT FOR THE SACRIFICE.

JUST THEN, THREE HUNGRY CROOKS HAPPENED TO SEE HIM.

WHAT A PLUMP GOAT!

IT WOULD MAKE A FINE DINNER! LET'S TRICK HIM OUT OF IT.

IT SHOULDN'T BE DIFFICULT. LISTEN, I'LL TELL YOU WHAT WE'LL DO.

THE FIRST CROOK WALKED UP TO THE BRAHMAN.

O BRAHMAN, HOW CAN YOU DEFILE YOURSELF BY CARRYING A DOG ON YOUR SHOULDER?

YOU FOOL! DON'T YOU KNOW A GOAT FROM A DOG?

NOW, NOW! KEEP YOUR TEMPER. YOU ARE WELCOME TO CARRY THE DOG IF YOU WISH.

ARE MY EYES PLAYING TRICKS ON ME? NO; TO BE SURE IT'S A GOAT!

THE BRAHMAN WALKED ON A LITTLE FARTHER WHEN THE SECOND CROOK STOPPED HIM.

WHY, HOLY SIR! THIS DEAD CALF MAY HAVE BEEN DEAR TO YOU...

...BUT MUST YOU CARRY IT ON YOUR SHOULDERS? HAVE YOU FORGOTTEN THAT YOU ARE A BRAHMAN?

ARE YOU BLIND? CAN'T YOU SEE THAT THIS IS A LIVE GOAT AND NOT A DEAD CALF?

PLEASE DON'T BE ANGRY, HOLY SIR. I'M SORRY. MY MISTAKE, PERHAPS.

WHAT'S THE MATTER? AM I MAD OR ARE THEY?

HARDLY HAD HE WALKED A FEW YARDS AHEAD WHEN—

O BRAHMAN, DROP THE DONKEY BEFORE ANYONE SEES YOU! PEOPLE WILL TALK.

NO! THREE OF THEM CANNOT BE WRONG!

THE BRAHMAN DID NOT UTTER A WORD. HE PULLED THE GOAT OFF HIS SHOULDERS, FLUNG IT TO THE GROUND . . .

...AND RAN AWAY AS FAST AS HE COULD.

THAT WAS NO GOAT! IT WAS A GOBLIN THAT KEPT CHANGING ITS SHAPE. HOW COULD THE VILLAGER PLAY SUCH A MEAN TRICK ON ME!

HA HA HO HO!   HO! HA!

AS SOON AS HE WAS OUT OF SIGHT —

COME ON, FRIENDS! THAT WAS NEATLY DONE. NOW YOU THERE, COLLECT STICKS AND LIGHT A FIRE. WE TWO SHALL KILL AND SKIN THE GOAT.

MORAL: TRUST YOURSELF BEFORE YOU TRUST OTHERS.

THE KING ELEPHANT AND THE MICE

ONE HOT SUMMER, ALL THE RIVERS IN A FOREST RAN DRY.

THE KING ELEPHANT OF A HERD OF ELEPHANTS WAS WORRIED.

IF I DON'T FIND SOME WATER SOON, WE WILL ALL DIE.

SUDDENLY, ONE OF HIS RETINUE LUMBERED UP TO HIM.

WATER! I KNOW WHERE WE CAN GET WATER. A BIRD TOLD ME THAT IN A LAKE NOT FAR FROM HERE, THERE IS ENOUGH WATER FOR TEN HERDS LIKE OURS!

THE KING WAS RELIEVED. HE GAVE ORDERS AND THE MARCH BEGAN.

YOU LEAD US, WE WILL FOLLOW.

TOWARDS NOON, THE ELEPHANTS SPOTTED THE LAKE.

LOOK! THERE IT IS!

AND THEY CHARGED TOWARDS THE WATER, TRAMPLING EVERYTHING IN THEIR WAKE.

RUN! RUN FOR YOUR LIVES!

ELEPHANTS! IT'S A STAMPEDE!

AMONG THE VICTIMS WERE A NUMBER OF MICE WHO HAD BURROWED A COLONY NEAR THE LAKE. LATER, THE MICE THAT HAD MANAGED TO ESCAPE, HELD A MEETING.

ONE OF THEM HAD AN IDEA.

WHY DON'T WE GO TO THE KING OF THE HERD AND REQUEST HIM NOT TO COME THIS WAY AGAIN?

AN EXCELLENT IDEA!

SO THEY WENT TO THE KING ELEPHANT.

O KING, WE HAVE BEEN LIVING NEAR THIS LAKE FOR GENERATIONS. WHILE YOUR HERD CAME CHARGING THIS WAY, IT TRAMPLED TO DEATH NEARLY HALF OUR CLAN. WE BEG OF YOU...

...HAVE MERCY ON US AND FIND SOME OTHER PATH TO AND FROM THE LAKE.

SPARE OUR LIVES. SMALL THOUGH WE ARE, SOME DAY WE MAY PROVE USEFUL TO YOU.

PAH! HOW CAN THESE TEENY-WEENY MICE BE USEFUL TO US?

BUT THE ELEPHANT WAS KIND-HEARTED.

SET YOUR MINDS AT REST. I SHALL TELL MY HERD TO TAKE ANOTHER PATH.

O KING, WE ARE GRATEFUL TO YOU. IF EVER YOU NEED US, WE SHALL BE WITH YOU.

AS HE WATCHED THE GRATEFUL, HAPPY MICE SCAMPER AWAY, LITTLE DID THE KING ELEPHANT REALISE HOW SOON HE WOULD NEED THEM!

A FEW DAYS LATER, AS THE ELEPHANTS LUMBERED TOWARDS THE LAKE AS USUAL—

CHEEEE

IT'S A TRAP!

TAKE CARE!

TRAPPERS ON OUR TRAIL!

THREE DAYS LATER, THE TRAPPERS CAME.

I WONDER HOW AND WITH WHOSE HELP WE WILL BE FREED; BUT FREE OUR-SELVES WE WILL.

SUDDENLY, HE REMEMBERED THE MICE.

MY FRIENDS THE MICE! WHY DIDN'T I THINK OF THEM EARLIER! BUT HOW SHALL I SEND A MESSAGE TO THEM?

AS SOON AS THE MICE HEARD THE ELEPHANT'S STORY—

WE WILL COME RIGHT AWAY. LEAD US TO THEM.

THAT NIGHT, WHEN ONE OF THE ELEPHANTS WHO HAD ESCAPED CAME TO SEE THE KING—

GO TO THE MICE AND TELL THEM OF OUR PLIGHT.

HURRY!

HURRY!

WE MUST FINISH OUR TASK BEFORE DAWN! BEFORE THE TRAPPERS RETURN!

AS SOON AS THEY REACHED THE PLACE WHERE THE ELEPHANTS WERE TIED UP...

...THEY GNAWED AWAY THE ROPES...

...AND WORKING ALL NIGHT, SET THE ELEPHANTS FREE BEFORE DAWN.

HOW WISE I WAS TO HAVE SPARED THEIR LIVES, INSIGNIFICANT AS THEY SEEMED.

MORAL: NEVER UNDERESTIMATE ANYBODY, HOWEVER SMALL HE MAY BE.

THE BRAHMAN, THE THIEF AND THE RAKSHASA

ONCE THERE WAS A BRAHMAN NAMED DRONA, WHO HAD GIVEN UP ALL THE LUXURIES OF LIFE.

ONE DAY, A DEVOTEE CAME TO SEE HIM.

MASTER, YOU ARE LEAN AND HUNGRY. PLEASE ACCEPT THESE.

TWO CALVES! MAY YOU EVER BE PROSPEROUS.

THE BRAHMAN FED THE CALVES ON BUTTER, OIL AND GRAIN. A THIEF NOTICED ALL THIS.

WHAT FAT CALVES! THIS VERY NIGHT, I SHALL STEAL THEM.

THAT NIGHT, AS HE WAS ON HIS WAY TO THE BRAHMAN'S HOUSE —

GOOD LORD! WHAT'S THIS?

I AM A RAKSHASA CALLED SATYAVACHANA. WHO ARE YOU?

I'M KRURAKARMA. I'M GOING TO STEAL TWO FAT CALVES FROM A POOR BRAHMAN.

I SEE. LET'S BE FRIENDS.

I'M VERY HUNGRY. I'LL EAT THE BRAHMAN WHILE YOU GET THE CALVES.

FINE! LET US GO!

SH! LET'S HIDE HERE AND WAIT.

I CAN HARDLY WAIT!

WHEN THE BRAHMAN BEGAN SNORING, THEY ENTERED THE HOUSE.

LET ME EAT HIM NOW! I'M HUNGRY.

NO, NO, LET US WAIT.

I'LL TAKE THE CALVES FIRST OR ELSE THE BRAHMAN WILL WAKE UP.

NO, NO! IF THE CALVES MOO, I'LL BE THE LOSER!

NO! I'LL TAKE THE CALVES FIRST!

NO! I'LL EAT THE BRAHMAN FIRST.

THE SOUND OF THEIR RAISED VOICES WOKE UP THE BRAHMAN.

WHAT'S THAT? WHO ARE YOU?

O BRAHMAN, THIS RAKSHASA WANTS TO EAT YOU!

THIS THIEF WANTS TO STEAL YOUR CALVES!

THE FRIGHTENED BRAHMAN INVOKED HIS DEITY.

O LORD, PLEASE DRIVE AWAY THE RAKSHASA.

IN AN INSTANT, THE RAKSHASA VANISHED.

AS FOR YOU, RUN OFF OR I'LL BEAT YOU UP!

THE THIEF IS GONE. THE CALVES ARE SAFE, AND I AM ALIVE! THANK GOD!

MORAL: WHEN YOUR ENEMIES QUARREL AMONGST THEMSELVES, YOU STAND TO GAIN.

THE LION, THE JACKAL AND THE CAVE

ONCE A LION CALLED KHARANAKHARA COULD NOT FIND ANYTHING TO EAT. HE WAS VERY HUNGRY.

ANOTHER DAY OF STARVATION! I CAN'T BEAR IT ANY MORE.

AT SUNSET, HE REACHED A BIG CAVE.

SOME ANIMAL MUST BE LIVING IN THIS CAVE. I'LL GO IN AND AWAIT ITS RETURN.

AS THE LION WAITED INSIDE THE CAVE, A JACKAL ARRIVED.

STRANGE! A LION'S FOOTPRINTS, LEADING INTO MY CAVE BUT NONE COMING OUT.

HOW CAN I FIND OUT IF A LION IS INSIDE OR NOT?

I HAVE IT! HELLO, CAVE!

WHY DON'T YOU ANSWER? IF YOU DON'T, I'LL GO ELSEWHERE.

WHEN THE LION HEARD THIS —

WHY DOESN'T THE CAVE REPLY? IS HE AFRAID OF ME?

I'D BETTER ANSWER FOR THE CAVE OR THE JACKAL MAY GO AWAY AND I'LL LOSE MY DINNER!

18

HELLO JACKAL. IT'S ALL RIGHT FOR YOU TO COME IN. PLEASE DO!

AS THE LION WAITED FOR A REPLY...

...THE FRIGHTENED JACKAL RAN TO SAFETY.

I'VE GROWN OLD IN THIS CAVE BUT NEVER BEFORE DID IT TALK!

MORAL: TO BE FOREWARNED IS TO BE FOREARMED.

THE MOUSE AND THE SAGE

LONG, LONG AGO, IN A HERMITAGE ON THE BANK OF THE RIVER GANGA, THERE LIVED A SAGE CALLED YAJNAVALKYA.

ONE DAY AS YAJNAVALKYA WAS SAYING HIS PRAYERS IN THE SACRED STREAM —

WHAT'S THIS! A MOUSE!

FOR A MOMENT, THE SAGE WONDERED WHAT TO DO WITH IT.

IF I LEAVE IT ON THE BANK, THE HAWK MAY ONCE AGAIN POUNCE ON IT.

THEN AN IDEA STRUCK HIM.

WHY NOT! AND MY WIFE HAS ALWAYS WANTED A DAUGHTER. YES. I'LL TURN IT INTO A BABY GIRL.

SO, USING HIS YOGIC POWERS, HE CHANGED THE MOUSE INTO A BABY GIRL AND TOOK HER HOME TO HIS WIFE.

TAKE HER, DEAR WIFE, AND REAR HER AS OUR OWN DAUGHTER.

AH! MY PRAYERS HAVE AT LAST BEEN ANSWERED.

THE GIRL GREW UP IN THE SAGE'S HOUSE. SOON SHE WAS TWELVE YEARS OLD.

DEAR HUSBAND, DON'T YOU THINK IT'S TIME WE FOUND A SUITABLE HUSBAND FOR OUR DAUGHTER?

YOU ARE RIGHT. I MUST GIVE HER TO SOMEONE REALLY WORTHY OF HER.

I WILL SUMMON THE SUN AND GIVE HER TO HIM.

A GOOD CHOICE.

AND YAJNAVALKYA SUMMONED HIM.

HOLY SIR, WHAT DO YOU WANT OF ME?

I WANT YOU TO MARRY MY DAUGHTER, IF SHE IS WILLING.

THEN THE SAGE TURNED TO HIS DAUGHTER.

WILL YOU MARRY THE SUN WHO GIVES LIGHT AND WARMTH TO ALL THE THREE WORLDS?

NO, FATHER. I DO NOT LIKE HIM BECAUSE HE IS TOO HOT. ISN'T THERE SOMEONE GREATER THAN HIM?

O BLESSED ONE, IS THERE ANYONE SUPERIOR TO YOU?

YES. THE CLOUD. HE CAN BLOT ME OUT WHENEVER HE FEELS LIKE IT.

SO THE SAGE SUMMONED THE CLOUD.

LITTLE GIRL, WILL YOU MARRY HIM?

NO, FATHER. HE IS DARK AND COLD. PLEASE FIND ME SOMEONE BETTER.

O CLOUD, IS THERE SOMEONE BETTER THAN YOU?

YES, THE WIND. HE CAN PUSH ME ABOUT AS HE PLEASES.

SO THE WIND WAS SUMMONED. BUT THE LITTLE GIRL DIDN'T WANT HIM EITHER.

I'M SORRY, FATHER. HOW CAN I MARRY HIM? HE'S ALWAYS RESTLESS.

O WIND, CAN YOU SUGGEST SOMEONE STEADY?

WHY, THE MOUNTAIN, OF COURSE! HE NEVER MOVES. TRY AS I MIGHT, I CAN'T PUSH HIM AROUND.

SO THE SAGE TOOK HIS DAUGHTER TO THE MOUNTAIN.

O MOUNTAIN! WILL YOU ACCEPT MY DAUGHTER FOR A WIFE?

GLADLY, O SAGE.

23

I SHALL MARRY YOU TO HIM, MY DAUGHTER. WHO COULD BE STEADIER THAN HIM?

BUT TO HIS SURPRISE, HIS DAUGHTER WAS ALMOST IN TEARS.

O FATHER, PLEASE SPARE ME. HE IS SO COARSE AND LIFELESS. PLEASE, PLEASE FIND SOMEONE MORE LIVELY.

THE SAGE LOOKED UP AT THE WISE MOUNTAIN.

O MIGHTY, WISE ONE, CAN YOU SUGGEST SOMEONE MORE SUITABLE?

OF COURSE, I CAN. THE BEST MATE FOR YOUR DAUGHTER WOULD BE THE KING OF THE MICE. HE'S THE LIVELIEST, FRISKIEST CREATURE I'VE SEEN IN MY LIFETIME. AND I AM MANY HUNDRED YEARS OLD.

SO THE SAGE SUMMONED THE KING OF THE MICE. AS SOON AS HE APPEARED, THE LITTLE GIRL QUIVERED WITH JOY.

FATHER, HE'S THE ONE I'LL MARRY. PLEASE TURN ME INTO A MOUSE SO THAT I CAN KEEP HOUSE FOR HIM AS A GOOD WIFE SHOULD.

THE SAGE USED HIS YOGIC POWERS AND TURNED HER BACK INTO A MOUSE.

HE THEN GAVE HER IN MARRIAGE TO THE KING OF THE MICE.

STRANGE ARE THE WAYS OF NATURE. I BROUGHT HER UP AS A HUMAN CHILD. I OFFERED HER THE SUN, THE CLOUD, THE WIND, THE MOUNTAIN; AND YET, SHE FOUND SHE COULD BE HAPPY ONLY WITH THE HUMBLE MOUSE.

MORAL: LET A MOUSE BE A MOUSE.

THE BIRD WHO SHED GOLDEN DROPPINGS

IN A HUGE TREE, THERE ONCE LIVED A BIRD CALLED SINDHUKA. ONE DAY, A HUNTER WHO HAD COME THERE TO CATCH BIRDS SAT DOWN TO REST UNDER THE TREE.

SUDDENLY —

CHEE! CHEE! A BIRD'S DROPPINGS!

AS HE BENT DOWN TO BRUSH OFF THE DROPPINGS —

WHAT! IT'S TURNED INTO GOLD!

JUST THEN THE BIRD FLEW AWAY.

AH! THAT MUST BE THE BRANCH WHERE IT USUALLY SITS. I'LL SET A TRAP RIGHT WHERE IT WAS PERCHING.

NEVER HAVE I SEEN THIS KIND OF THING BEFORE. I MUST CATCH THAT BIRD.

SO HE SET THE TRAP AND WAITED.

THAT EVENING, WHEN THE BIRD RETURNED HOME TO ROOST, IT DID NOT EXAMINE ITS PERCH FOR ANY LURKING DANGER AS A GOOD BIRD SHOULD.

THE NEXT MOMENT, THE NET HAD FALLEN OVER IT.

THE HUNTER PUT THE BIRD INTO A CAGE.

I'LL TAKE HIM HOME. I'LL NEVER HAVE TO HUNT AGAIN.

ON THE WAY HOME, HOWEVER, HE HAD SECOND THOUGHTS.

SUPPOSING SOMEONE SEES IT AND TELLS THE KING.

THE KING WOULD BE ANGRY WITH ME FOR NOT TELLING HIM ABOUT IT.

HE MIGHT EVEN BEHEAD ME! NO, MY LIFE IS WORTH MORE THAN ALL THE GOLD IN THE WORLD.

THE HUNTER WAS CONVINCED THAT HIS LIFE WOULD BE IN DANGER IF HE KEPT THE BIRD.

I'LL TAKE THE BIRD TO THE KING AND SAVE MY LIFE!

AT THE PALACE —

YOUR MAJESTY, I HAVE BROUGHT YOU A RARE GIFT. THE DROPPINGS OF THIS BIRD TURN INTO GOLD THE MOMENT THEY TOUCH SOMETHING.

THE KING WAS DELIGHTED WITH HIS GIFT. HE TURNED TO HIS ATTENDANTS —

LOOK AFTER THIS BIRD WITH THE UTMOST CARE. GIVE HIM WHATEVER HE WANTS TO EAT AND DRINK.

THE MINISTERS, HOW-EVER, DID NOT QUITE LIKE A MERE BIRD GETTING SO MUCH ATTENTION.

O KING, IT IS NOT WISE TO TRUST THE WORDS OF A MERE HUNTER. HOW CAN A BIRD'S DROPPINGS TURN INTO GOLD?

BLINDED BY JEALOUSY, THEY GAVE THE KING FOOLISH COUNSEL.

IT IS CRUEL TO CAGE THIS POOR BIRD BECAUSE OF WHAT THAT HUNTER SAYS. BIRDS SHOULD BE FLYING FREELY IN THE FOREST.

HOW RIGHT THEY ARE!

THE FOOLISH KING TRUSTED THE MINISTER'S WORDS WITHOUT FINDING OUT THE FACTS FOR HIMSELF.

ALL RIGHT, THEN SET IT FREE.

AN ATTENDANT OPENED THE CAGE.

THE DELIGHTED BIRD FLEW TO THE TOP OF THE TALL PALACE GATES···

···AND PERCHING HIMSELF THERE, LET FALL HIS DROPPINGS.

WHY! THE DROPPINGS HAVE, INDEED, TURNED TO GOLD! FOOLS THAT WE ARE! QUICK! GET THE BIRD.

BUT THE BIRD FLEW AWAY.

NOT AGAIN, MY KING. WE HAVE ALL BEEN A PACK OF FOOLS; FIRST I, THEN THE HUNTER, THEN YOUR MINISTERS AND THEN YOU. NO, I'LL NOT BE SO FOOLISH AS TO BE CAUGHT AGAIN.

MORAL: ASCERTAIN A FACT BEFORE YOU ACCEPT ANOTHER'S WORD FOR IT.

Illustrated Classics From India

No god in the Hindu pantheon has inspired more passion and devotion than Krishna. Famed for his love of humanity, Krishna is at once the eternal child, the brave warrior, the faithful friend and the intense lover. With a flute to his lips and a mischievous sparkle in his eyes, Krishna continues to inspire and enthral his devotees, protecting them even as he sustains order in the universe.

Bhagawat
The Krishna Avatar

272 large-size, four-colour pages, in hard-bound deluxe edition.
Add Rs 30 on all outstation cheques.

Rs 280 Only

INDIA BOOK HOUSE PVT LTD

Mahalaxmi Chambers, 5th Floor, 22 Bhulabhai Desai Road,
Mumbai 400 026, India. Tel 2352 5636, 2352 3409
Email : info@amarchitrakatha.com

AMAR CHITRA KATHA

Panchatantra
Crows and Owls

Illustrated Classics From India

Panchatantra
Crows and owls and other stories

The original text of the Panchatantra in Sanskrit was probably written about 200 B.C. by a great Hindi scholar, Pandit Vishnu Sharma. Some of the tales themselves could be much older, their origin going back to the period of the Vedas and the Upanishads (1500 B.C. to 500 B.C.). In the course of time, travellers took these stories with them to Persia and Arabia and finally, through Greece, to Europe. So far the Panchatantra has been translated into more than 50 languages of the world.

The Panchatantra is essentially connected with one of the branches of science known to us as the Nitishastra or 'A book of wise conduct in life'. It attempts to teach us how to understand people, how to choose reliable and trustworthy friends, how to overcome difficulties and solve problems through tact and wisdom, how to live in peace and harmony in the face of hypocrisy, deceit and the many pitfalls that are encountered in life.

The Panchatantra is woven around the tale of a king who entrusts his three dull sons to a Brahman called Pandit Vishnu Sharma, to illuminate their minds with knowledge and wisdom in a short six months. The Brahman promises to educate them and takes them to his ashrama (hermitage). There he recites to them his specially composed tales, divided into five tantras (literally, five systems) on how to deal with people in life.

The Panchatantra is a rare book, for in no other book can one find philosophy, psychology, politics, music, astronomy, human relations, etc. all discussed together in a simple yet elegant style. This is exactly what Pandit Vishnu Sharma had in mind – to impart as much knowledge to the princes in as uncomplicated a manner as possible. And, indeed, for the past 2,200 years, not only the princes but also millions of listeners and readers have benefited from his unique books.

Script: Luis M. Fernandes   Illustrations: M. Mohandas   Cover: C.M. Vitankar

CROWS AND OWLS

A COLONY OF CROWS DWELT IN A GREAT BANYAN TREE IN A FOREST. THE NAME OF THEIR KING WAS CLOUDY.

THE CROWS WERE CONSTANTLY HARASSED BY THEIR POWERFUL ENEMIES, THE OWLS. THEIR KING, FOE-CRUSHER WOULD ATTACK ANY CROW HE CAME ACROSS.

WHOOO-OOOO-IT!

THEN ONE DAY, CLOUDY CALLED A MEETING OF HIS FIVE COUNSELLORS.

THE OWLS ARE BECOMING A MENACE.

THEY ARE ARROGANT AND POWERFUL AND THEY ATTACK US AT NIGHT WHEN WE CANNOT SEE. WE CANNOT COUNTER-ATTACK DURING THE DAY BECAUSE WE DON'T KNOW WHERE THEY DWELL.

ADVISE ME, COUNSELLORS. WHAT SHOULD WE DO?

1

LET US SUE FOR PEACE. IT IS ALWAYS ADVISABLE TO MAKE PEACE WITH POWERFUL FOES.

I DON'T AGREE.

ONE SHOULD NEVER MAKE PEACE WITH WICKED CREATURES. LET US DECLARE WAR ON THE RASCALS!

THE ENEMY IS VICIOUS AND POWERFUL. I ADVISE NEITHER PEACE NOR WAR BUT A CHANGE OF RESIDENCE. LET US GO AWAY FROM HERE.

GO AWAY WHERE?

A CROCODILE IF HE STAYS AT HOME CAN DEFEAT AN ELEPHANT.

BUT IF HE LEAVES HIS SWAMP, EVEN A DOG CAN MAKE HIM RUN. I SAY, LET US STAY HERE AND FORTIFY OUR POSITIONS!

IN MY HUMBLE OPINION WE SHOULD FORM ALLIANCES WITH OTHER FRIENDLY BIRDS.

THEN CLOUDY TURNED TO A VERY OLD CROW NAMED LIVE-STRONG.

AND WHAT DO YOU ADVISE, REVERED SIR?

I ADVISE DUPLICITY, MY LORD.

ATTACK ME AT ONCE WITH A GREAT SHOW OF ANGER.

ATTACK YOU? MY WISEST MINISTER?

YES. WE MUST PUT UP THIS SHOW FOR THE BENEFIT OF OUR FRIEND OVER THERE.

AN OWL!

LET HIM THINK WE'VE FALLEN OUT. THROW ME OUT OF THE TREE. THEN, WITH ALL YOUR SUBJECTS...

...FLY TO ANTELOPE MOUNTAIN.

AND WHAT WILL YOU DO?

I WILL BEFRIEND THE OWLS AND WIN THEIR TRUST. AND THEN I'LL FIND A WAY TO BRING ABOUT THEIR DOOM.

3

NOW DO AS I SAY, YOU COWARD!

!

HOW DARE HE SPEAK LIKE THAT TO OUR KING!

?

I'LL WRING HIS NECK FOR HIM.

LEAVE HIM TO ME.

SO YOU HAVE TURNED TRAITOR! WE DON'T WANT ANY TRAITORS HERE!

AH, THEY ARE FIGHTING AMONGST THEMSELVES.

GET OUT! —AND STAY OUT!

4

THE OWL LOST NO TIME IN REPORTING WHAT HE HAD HEARD AND SEEN TO HIS MASTER, KING FOE-CRUSHER.

YOUR MAJESTY, THE CROWS ARE FIGHTING AMONGST THEMSELVES.

THEY HAVE THROWN OUT ONE OF THEIR MINISTERS.

THEN THIS IS A GOOD TIME TO ATTACK THEM. A DISORGANISED ENEMY IS EASILY DEFEATED.

FOLLOW ME, MY FRIENDS.

FOE-CRUSHER AND HIS OWLS ATTACKED THE BANYAN TREE WITH BLOODCURDLING WAR CRIES.

WHOOOO!

WHOOO-IEEEE!

BUT THEY SOON REALISED THAT THERE WAS NOT A SINGLE CROW IN THE TREE.

THE COWARDS HAVE FLED!

OLD LIVE-STRONG WHO HAD BEEN WATCHING THE PROCEEDINGS FROM THE GROUND WAS PLEASED WITH THE WAY THINGS WERE GOING.

THE FIRST PART OF MY PLAN HAS SUCCEEDED.

NEXT COMES THE MOST DANGEROUS PART... BUT THERE'S NO TURNING BACK NOW.

WELL, HERE GOES.

CAW! CAW!

LOOK, A CROW!

I AM NO ORDINARY CROW. I AM CLOUDY'S MINISTER. BE GOOD ENOUGH TO INFORM YOUR MASTER OF MY PRESENCE.

I HAVE MUCH TO DISCUSS WITH HIM.

I'LL FETCH HIM.

THE OWL SOON RETURNED WITH FOE-CRUSHER WHO WAS ASTONISHED TO SEE THE BATTERED CONDITION OF THE OLD CROW.

HOW HAVE YOU COME TO SUCH A SORRY STATE, MY DEAR SIR?

THIS IS THE WAY I HAVE BEEN REWARDED FOR GIVING GOOD ADVICE, YOUR MAJESTY.

MY MASTER, CLOUDY, BECAME FURIOUS WITH ME WHEN I URGED HIM TO PAY YOU TRIBUTE. HE ASSAULTED ME AND THREW ME OUT OF THE TREE.

HENCEFORTH I SHALL WORK FOR THE DESTRUCTION OF ALL CROWS. NOW I THROW MYSELF AT YOUR MERCY.

I WILL TALK IT OVER WITH MY ADVISERS.

FOE-CRUSHER HAD FIVE ANCESTRAL COUNSELLORS. THEIR NAMES WERE RED-EYE, FIERCE-EYE, HOOK-NOSE, FLAME-EYE AND WALL-EAR.

THE CROW SEEKS ASYLUM. WHAT IS YOUR OPINION, RED-EYE?

SLAY HIM WITHOUT FURTHER DELAY, MY LORD. HE IS A CROW!

BUT THE OTHER COUNSELLORS WERE MORE CHARITABLE.

GRANT HIM REFUGE, O KING!

IT WOULD BE WRONG TO KILL ONE WHO SEEKS YOUR PROTECTION.

HE MAY PROVE USEFUL TO US IN OUR WAR WITH THE CROWS.

DO NOT LISTEN TO THEM, YOUR MAJESTY. SLAY HIM! HE IS UP TO NO GOOD!

I HAVE ALREADY MADE UP MY MIND, RED-EYE. THE CROW STAYS WITH US. WE SHALL TAKE HIM TO OUR FORTRESS.

THE OWLS LIFTED UP LIVE-STRONG AND CARRIED HIM TO THEIR FORTRESS.

I HAVE FOOLED THEM ALL EXCEPT THE SHREWD RED-EYE. HE HAS GUESSED MY TRUE PURPOSE.

THIS IS OUR FORTRESS, SIR. HERE YOU MAY STAY IN COMFORT AND HONOUR.

HO, THERE! MAKE OUR GUEST COMFORTABLE. LOOK AFTER HIS NEEDS.

IF I STAY IN THEIR MIDST IT WILL BE DIFFICULT FOR ME TO GO ABOUT MY BUSINESS WITHOUT BEING OBSERVED.

O KING, IT WOULD NOT BE PROPER FOR ME TO ENTER YOUR FORTRESS. I AM, AFTER ALL, A CROW AND UNWORTHY OF THE HONOUR.

GIVE ME A LITTLE PLACE NEAR THE GATE AND THAT IS ENOUGH.

YOU MAY STAY NEAR THE GATE IF IT PLEASES YOU, MY FRIEND.

THE SECOND PART OF MY PLAN HAS GONE THROUGH SUCCESSFULLY. I CAN COME AND GO AS I WISH.

LIVE-STRONG MADE HIMSELF COMFORTABLE NEAR THE GATE AND BEGAN TO ENJOY A LIFE OF EASE AND COMFORT, UNPERTURBED BY RED-EYE'S HOSTILITY.

HAVE SOME RICE, YOUR HONOUR.

AND HERE ARE SOME MANGOES.

HOW THEY PAMPER HIM. IT MAKES ME SICK!

WE ARE FATTENING HIM WHILE HE IS PLANNING OUR DESTRUCTION. HE MUST BE LAUGHING AT US.

YOUR MAJESTY, THE CROW MUST GO! HE IS MAKING A FOOL OF YOU!

RED-EYE!

10

LEAVE THAT POOR CREATURE ALONE. HE IS HARMLESS.

THEY WON'T LISTEN TO ME. I CAN'T STAY HERE ANY LONGER.

RED-EYE GATHERED HIS FOLLOWERS AND TOLD THEM TO PACK UP THEIR BELONGINGS.

THE END IS AT HAND. I CANNOT SAVE THE KING AS HE REFUSES TO BE GUIDED BY ME. LET US, AT LEAST, SAVE OURSELVES WHILE WE CAN.

ANYONE WHO CONTINUES TO LIVE HERE DOES SO AT HIS OWN PERIL. LET US GO FORTH AND SEEK ANOTHER FORTRESS IN THE MOUNTAINS.

LIVE-STRONG WAS OVERJOYED WHEN HE SAW RED-EYE LEAVING THE FORTRESS WITH HIS FOLLOWERS.

ONLY HE COULD HAVE FOILED MY PLANS. THE REST OF THEM ARE NUMSKULLS.

THE DAYS OF THE OWLS ARE NUMBERED. FROM TOMORROW I SHALL START BUILDING MY NEST OF DEATH.

EACH DAY THEREAFTER, LIVE-STRONG WENT INTO THE FOREST AND RETURNED WITH A TWIG WHICH HE DROPPED INSIDE THE GATE.

I AM BUILDING A NEST, YOUR MAJESTY. I HOPE YOU DO NOT MIND.

OF COURSE, NOT!

LET US KNOW IF YOU NEED ANY HELP.

SOON THERE WAS A LARGE PILE OF TWIGS AT THE GATE, BUT NONE OF THE OWLS STOPPED TO WONDER WHY THEIR GUEST REQUIRED SO BIG A NEST.

THEN ONE MORNING WHEN THE OWLS WERE ASLEEP, LIVE-STRONG QUIETLY LEFT THE FORTRESS.

HE FLEW DIRECTLY TO A NEARBY MOUNTAIN WHERE CLOUDY AND THE OTHER CROWS WERE WAITING FOR HIM.

WE ARE DELIGHTED TO SEE YOU BACK WITH US!

HOW WAS YOUR STAY WITH THE OWLS?

I SHALL GIVE YOU A FULL ACCOUNT OF MY ADVENTURES LATER, MY LORD.

BUT WE HAVE WORK TO DO NOW. LET EVERY CROW TAKE UP A BURNING TWIG AND COME WITH US.

SOON, AN ARMY OF CROWS LED BY THE TIRELESS LIVE-STRONG WAS STREAKING THROUGH THE MORNING SKY.

THERE'S THE CAVE. DROP YOUR TWIGS ON THE NEST AND SET IT ON FIRE.

THE CROWS DID AS THEY WERE TOLD.

THUD

13

AND SOON—

FIRE! THE CAVE IS ON FIRE!

THE OWLS, STILL HALF ASLEEP, TRIED TO RUSH OUT OF THE CAVE BUT WERE BEATEN BACK BY THE FLAMES.

THE CROW HAS DONE THIS! I SHOULD HAVE LISTENED TO MY FAITHFUL RED-EYE!

WE ARE DOOMED! DOOMED!

AH!

THE CAVE, CLOSED AS IT WAS FROM ALL SIDES, BECAME A FIERY FURNACE.

THOSE OF THE OWLS WHO MANAGED TO EVADE THE FLAMES WERE SUFFOCATED BY THE FUMES. ALL OF THEM, INCLUDING KING FOE-CRUSHER, PERISHED.

AND THUS DID THE CROWS RID THEMSELVES OF THEIR POWERFUL BUT DIM-WITTED ENEMIES, THE OWLS.

14

THE NOBLE ENEMY

A MAN WAS SEARCHING FOR GEMS ON THE TOP OF A CERTAIN MOUNTAIN.

AFTER A LONG UNSUCCESSFUL SEARCH, HE WAS EXHAUSTED AND THREW HIMSELF ON THE GROUND BEHIND A ROCK.

I'LL TAKE A SHORT NAP AND THEN TRY AGAIN.

BZZ...BZZ...BZZ...

...TOO MANY DACOITS AROUND HERE...

...THE GEMS...

GOOD GOD! THOSE YOUNG MEN HAVE FOUND SOME GEMS!

...WOULD BE SAFEST... IN OUR STOMACHS!

THEY ARE SWALLOWING THEM!

THIS IS NOT FAIR AT ALL. I SHOULD GET SOME GEMS TOO FOR MY TROUBLE.

I KNOW WHAT! I'LL MAKE FRIENDS WITH THESE FELLOWS AND WHEN THEY ARE ASLEEP, I'LL SLIT OPEN THEIR BELLIES AND TAKE THE GEMS.

LOOK, THERE'S A MAN FOLLOWING US.

GOOD MASTERS, I AM FORTUNATE TO HAVE MET YOU.

I AM ALONE AND I WAS LOOKING FOR COMPANY ON THIS DANGEROUS ROAD.

YOU ARE WELCOME TO TRAVEL WITH US, MY FRIEND.

16

THE MORE, THE MERRIER.

GOOD. THEY DON'T SUSPECT ANYTHING.

NOW ALL I HAVE TO DO IS WAIT FOR THE RIGHT MOMENT.

BUT UNFORTUNATELY FOR HIM, THAT MOMENT WAS NEVER TO COME. FOR AS THEY PASSED A VILLAGE THAT LAY ALONG THEIR ROUTE...

...A BIRD IN A ROBBER CHIEF'S HUT BEGAN TO SING.

THEY HAVE GEMS WITH THEM...THEY HAVE GEMS...

GEMS!

SEIZE THOSE MEN! BRING THEM HERE!

THE THREE FRIENDS AND THEIR COMPANIONS WERE CAPTURED AND BROUGHT BEFORE HIM.

I KNOW YOU HAVE GEMS WITH YOU. HAND THEM OVER.

WHAT! GEMS?

SEARCH THEM!

THE MEN SEARCHED THEIR CAPTIVES THOROUGHLY.

THERE HAS BEEN SOME MISTAKE. WE DON'T HAVE ANY GEMS WITH US!

WE CAN'T FIND ANYTHING ON THEM, CHIEF.

HOW'S THAT!

OH, WELL! THE BIRD MUST HAVE BEEN MISTAKEN.

ALL RIGHT. LET THEM GO.

BUT AS SOON AS THEY LEFT, THE BIRD BEGAN TO SING THE SAME SONG AGAIN.

THEY HAVE GEMS WITH THEM... THEY HAVE GEMS WITH THEM...

WHAT! HAVE THEY DECEIVED ME, THEN?

GO AFTER THEM! BRING THEM BACK!

THE FOUR MEN WERE BROUGHT BACK AND SEARCHED AGAIN.

NO! NOTHING ON THEM.

HOW CAN THAT BE? MY BIRD INSISTS...

AHA!

THE GEMS MUST BE IN YOUR STOMACHS! YOU HAVE SWALLOWED THEM!

ULP! WE ARE DONE FOR!

TAKE THEM AWAY AND CUT OPEN THEIR BELLIES.

NO, NO!

I AM BEYOND HELP. WHEN THEY FIND GEMS IN THEIR STOMACHS THEY WILL CUT OPEN MINE TOO.

ON THE OTHER HAND, THEY MAY CUT ME FIRST. EITHER WAY I AM DOOMED.

BUT I COULD SAVE THE OTHER FELLOWS. LET ME TRY...

YOU WON'T FIND ANY GEMS IN OUR STOMACHS, SIR. BUT IF YOU INSIST ON SEEING FOR YOURSELF LET ME BE THE FIRST TO DIE.

IT WOULD BE UNBEARABLE FOR ME TO WATCH THE STOMACHS OF MY FRIENDS BEING CUT OPEN.

WHETHER YOU DIE FIRST OR LAST MAKES NO DIFFERENCE TO ME.

TAKE HIM AWAY AND GRANT HIM HIS WISH.

THANK YOU.

IF MY LITTLE TRICK WORKS, MY DEATH WILL NOT HAVE BEEN IN VAIN.

THE MAN WAS TAKEN AWAY. LATER—

THERE WASN'T A SINGLE GEM IN HIS STOMACH.

WHAT!

SO MY BIRD CAN MAKE A MISTAKE AFTER ALL.

THERE WERE NO GEMS IN HIS STOMACH. THERE WON'T BE ANY IN THE STOMACHS OF HIS FRIENDS EITHER.

THERE HAS BEEN A TERRIBLE MISTAKE, MY FRIENDS. I AM SORRY THAT YOUR COMRADE IS DEAD.

YOU MAY GO.

LITTLE DID THE CHIEF REALISE THAT HE HAD DONE EXACTLY WHAT THE DEAD MAN HAD HOPED HE WOULD DO.

THE FRIENDS TOO, UNAWARE THAT THEY HAD BEEN SAVED BY A CLEVER RUSE, THOUGHT THEY HAD JUST BEEN VERY LUCKY, AND LOST NO TIME IN GETTING OUT OF THE VILLAGE.

MORAL: A SENSIBLE ENEMY CAN OFTEN PROVE TO BE YOUR BEST FRIEND.

THE BIRD AND THE MONKEYS

ONE CHILLY WINTER EVENING—

BRRR—RRR... IT'S COLD.

LOOK, BROTHER! A SPARK OF FIRE.

IT WAS A GLOW-WORM GOING PAST.

I'VE GOT IT!

PUT IT UNDER THIS PILE OF LEAVES.

WE WILL SOON HAVE A BIG BLAZING FIRE TO KEEP OURSELVES WARM.

YOU ARE MAKING A MISTAKE, GOOD SIRS.

THAT'S A FIREFLY YOU'VE CAUGHT...

...NOT A SPARK OF FIRE.

IGNORE HER!

LET'S BLOW ON THE LEAVES. THEY'LL CATCH FIRE FASTER THAT WAY.

LISTEN TO ME, SIRS...

...YOU ARE WASTING YOUR TIME AND ENERGY.

YOU CAN'T SET ANYTHING ALIGHT WITH A FIREFLY.

WHY DON'T YOU...

...STOP PESTERING US, YOU STUPID CREATURE!

DON'T TRY TO TEACH US HOW TO LIGHT A FIRE!

COME ON BROTHERS, LET'S GET BACK TO THE TASK.

PHOOOO!

PHOOOOOO!

MORAL: DON'T TRY TO TEACH THOSE WHO CANNOT BE TAUGHT.

THE CAMEL WHO WAS BEGUILED BY HIS COMPANIONS

A MERCHANT WAS LEADING A CARAVAN OF HEAVILY-LADEN CAMELS THROUGH A JUNGLE...

...WHEN ONE OF THEM, OVERCOME BY FATIGUE, COLLAPSED.

LET US SHIFT HIS LOAD ONTO THE OTHERS AND BE OFF. WE MUST NOT LET THIS LAZY CREATURE DELAY US.

LATER, WHEN THE CAMEL RECOVERED HIS STRENGTH —

THEY HAVE GONE! AND I AM ALONE IN THIS STRANGE JUNGLE.

FORTUNATELY, THERE'S PLENTY OF GRASS HERE. AT LEAST I WON'T STARVE.

DAYS PASSED AND THE CAMEL SOMEHOW SURVIVED THE PERILS OF THE JUNGLE.

THEN ONE DAY, A LION FOLLOWED BY A LEOPARD, A JACKAL AND A CROW, CAME BY.

24

MY GOD! WHAT STRANGE CREATURE IS THAT!

THAT IS A CAMEL, O KING.

THEY ARE NOT USUALLY FOUND IN JUNGLES.

LET US FIND OUT WHAT HE IS DOING HERE.

WHEN THE CAMEL TOLD THEM HIS STORY—

POOR FELLOW! HE HAS BEEN TREATED VERY BADLY.

YOU HAVE NOTHING TO FEAR NOW, MY FRIEND. HENCEFORTH YOU ARE UNDER MY PROTECTION. COME WITH US.

SO THE CAMEL JOINED THE LION'S ENTOURAGE AND WAS HAPPY TO HAVE FOUND SUCH A STRONG PROTECTOR.

BUT ONE DAY THE LION WAS WOUNDED IN A COMBAT WITH AN ELEPHANT. HE HAD TO RETIRE TO HIS CAVE AND THERE HE REMAINED FOR SEVERAL DAYS...

...MUCH TO THE DISMAY OF THE CROW, THE JACKAL AND THE LEOPARD WHO DEPENDED ON HIM FOR FOOD.

NO MEAT TODAY EITHER.

WE'LL STARVE TO DEATH AT THIS RATE.

THEY LOOK SO SAD. THEY MUST BE WORRYING ABOUT MY HEALTH. I WISH I COULD FEED THEM AS ALWAYS.

I AM SORRY I CANNOT PROVIDE YOU WITH FOOD NOW, MY FRIENDS. I AM TOO WEAK TO HUNT.

YOU WILL HAVE TO FEND FOR YOURSELVES TILL I RECOVER.

WHAT ARE YOU SAYING, MASTER?

HOW COULD WE EVEN THINK OF EATING WHEN YOU ARE STARVING!

THE LION WAS PLEASED WITH THE JACKAL'S REPLY.

YOU HAVE SHOWN YOURSELVES TO BE LOYAL SERVANTS. GO AND ROUND UP AN ANIMAL AND DRIVE IT THIS WAY SO THAT I MAY KILL IT FOR FOOD.

THE JACKAL AND HIS FRIENDS SCOURED THE JUNGLE BUT COULD NOT FIND ANY ANIMAL.

FINALLY, THEY FOUND THEMSELVES BACK WHERE THEY HAD STARTED.

THERE'S REALLY... ...NO NEED... TO EXERT OURSELVES LIKE THIS.

WHAT ELSE CAN WE DO?

WELL, THERE'S THE CAMEL. HIS FLESH COULD SUSTAIN US ALL FOR SEVERAL DAYS.

FORGET IT. THE KING WILL NEVER HURT ANY ANIMAL THAT IS UNDER HIS PROTECTION.

I'LL HAVE A WORD WITH HIM IN ANY CASE.

O KING, WE COULD NOT FIND AN ANIMAL FOR YOU. BUT THERE'S NO NEED FOR YOU TO STARVE.

YOU CAN EAT THE CAMEL.

WHAT!

ARE YOU SUGGESTING THAT I HURT AN ANIMAL THAT IS UNDER MY PROTECTION?

GET OUT OF MY SIGHT, YOU WRETCH!

PLEASE DON'T MISUNDERSTAND ME, O KING.

I WAS ONLY THINKING OF YOUR WELFARE. OUR OWN LIVES ARE WORTHLESS WHEN YOURS IS AT STAKE.

I KNOW IT WOULD BE WRONG FOR YOU TO HURT THE CAMEL IN ORDINARY CIRCUMSTANCES.

BUT WHAT IF HE HIMSELF DEVOTEDLY OFFERED HIS FLESH TO YOU? THEN NO ONE COULD BLAME YOU FOR SLAYING HIM.

I SUPPOSE YOU ARE RIGHT.

IF THE CAMEL WERE TO MAKE SUCH AN OFFER I MIGHT ACCEPT IT.

THE WILY JACKAL RAN BACK TO HIS FRIENDS WHO HAD NOW BEEN JOINED BY THE CAMEL.

FRIENDS, OUR KING IS DYING OF STARVATION. LET US GO AND BEG HIM TO EAT ONE OF US.

IT IS THE LEAST WE CAN DO FOR SUCH A NOBLE SOUL.

WHAT IS IT, MY FRIENDS? HAVE YOU CAUGHT ANY CREATURE?

28

NO, O KING. WE WERE NOT ABLE TO CATCH ANY CREATURE. YOU MAY EAT ANY ONE OF US INSTEAD.

AND THAT ONE WILL BE THE CAMEL!

I HOPE BROTHER LEOPARD TOO, CATCHES ON!

EAT ME, MASTER AND PROLONG YOUR LIFE FOR A DAY.

NO, NO, YOU'RE TOO SMALL. THE MASTER'S HUNGER WOULD HARDLY BE APPEASED BY EATING YOU.

EAT ME, MASTER.

AS IF YOU'RE VERY BIG YOURSELF.

IT IS ME YOU SHOULD EAT, MASTER.

ALL OF THEM HAVE OFFERED TO LAY DOWN THEIR LIVES FOR THE KING, BUT HE HAS NOT HURT ANY OF THEM.

NOW LET ME TOO MAKE A NOBLE GESTURE. THEY'LL PROTECT ME TOO!

SO THE POOR CAMEL STEPPED FORWARD.

STAND ASIDE, FRIEND LEOPARD. HOW CAN THE MASTER EAT YOU? YOU AND HE BELONG TO THE SAME FAMILY—WELL ALMOST.

EAT ME, MASTER.

AN OMINOUS SILENCE GREETED THE CAMEL'S OFFER. THEN—

I ACCEPT YOUR OFFER, O NOBLE CAMEL.

WHA...?!

BEFORE THE CAMEL COULD GET OVER HIS SHOCK, THE THREE ANIMALS RUSHED AT HIM...

...AND KILLED HIM. THUS DID THREE ROGUES TAKE ADVANTAGE OF THE TRUST REPOSED IN THEM BY A COMRADE.

MORAL: WATCH YOUR STEP WITH FALSE FRIENDS.

30

Amar Chitra Katha is a collection of illustrated classics that retell stories from Indian mythology, history, folktale and legend, through the fascinating medium of comics. Over 400 titles have been published in the Amar Chitra Katha comic series that are approved by parents, appreciated by children and accepted by schools.

Mythology

501 Krishna	525 Tales of Arjuna	570 Dasharatha
502 Hanuman	531 Karna	571 Dhruva and Ashtavakra
510 Buddha	533 Abhimanyu	572 Ancestors of Rama
511 Savitri	547 Garuda	589 Krishna and Shishupala
512 Tales of Vishnu	565 Drona	592 Ghatotkacha
520 Tales of Narada	566 Surya	612 Urvashi
524 Indra and Shibi	567 Indra and Shachi	663 Aniruddha

Folktales

507 Nala Damayanti	558 Birbal the Clever	607 A Bag of Gold Coins
523 Raman of Tenali	559 Birbal the Just	621 Udayana
543 Jataka Tales: Monkey Stories	578 Kesari the Flying Thief	625 Battle of Wits
553 Jataka Tales: Jackal Stories	580 Inimitable Birbal	659 Devi Choudhurani
554 Jataka Tales: Elephant Stories	581 Raman the Matchless Wit	664 King Kusha
555 Jataka Tales: Deer Stories	584 Gopal the Jester	667 Bikal the Terrible
557 Birbal the Witty	587 Birbal the Genius	713 The Fool's Disciples

History

508 Chanakya	606 Rani Durgavati	685 Chand Bibi
536 Ashoka	627 Harsha	701 Noor Jahan
563 Rana Pratap	630 Rana Sanga	704 Jallianwala Bagh
568 Vikramaditya	632 Vidyasagar	722 Megasthenes
579 Madhvacharya	648 Samudra Gupta	723 Jnaneshwar
603 Akbar	676 Rana Kumbha	725 Sultana Razia
604 Prithviraj Chauhan	682 Tanaji	734 Banda Bahadur

Biography

517 Vivekananda	564 Shivaji	647 Lal Bahadur Shastri
535 Mirabai	608 Bhagat Singh	650 Mahatma Gandhi
539 Rani of Jhansi	611 Babasaheb Ambedkar	678 Veer Savarkar
544 Subhas Chandra Bose	613 Soordas	679 Swami Pranavananda
548 Rabindranath Tagore	631 Chaitanya Mahaprabhu	693 Jayaprakash Narayan
551 Tulsidas	636 Krishnadeva Raya	700 Jawaharlal Nehru
563 Rana Pratap	645 Lokamanya Tilak	732 Swami Chinmayananda

Visit www.AmarChitraKatha.com for details on how to order these titles online.

INDIA BOOK HOUSE

Mahalaxmi Chambers, 5th Floor, 22 Bhulabhai Desai Road, Mumbai 400 026, India
Tel 23523827 Fax 23538406 Email info@amarchitrakatha.com

Illustrated Classics from India

NOW AVAILABLE ONLINE!

AmarChitraKatha.com
Illustrated Classics from India

Login   Search Search books..   G

New Reprints

Children's Corner

The Ramayana has remained the guiding light for ideal relationships and moral values of India

Festival Focus

GUDI PADWA

About Us   Catalogue   Feedback   Contact Us

The magic of the colourful tales of Amar Chitra Katha has woven nostalgic bonds among the Indian diaspora all over the globe. The Amar Chitra Katha comic books help Indians remain tethered to their roots, while making their mark as citizens of the world.

Order from the complete catalogue at a special online price, and also access heaps of information on Indian heritage and culture.

www.AmarChitraKatha.com

INDIA BOOK HOUSE

Mahalaxmi Chambers, 5th Floor, 22 Bhulabhai Desai Road, Mumbai 400 026, India
Tel 23523827 Fax 23538406 Email info@amarchitrakatha.com

AMAR CHITRA KATHA

Panchatantra
How the Jackal ate the Elephant
and other Stories

Illustrated Classics From India

Panchatantra
How the Jackal ate the Elephant and Other Stories

The original text of the Panchatantra in Sanskrit was written about 200 B.C. by a great Hindi scholar, Pandit Vishnu Sharma. Some of the tales themselves must be much older, their origin going back to the period of the Vedas and the Upanishads (1500 B.C. to 500 B.C.). In course of time, travellers took these stories with them to Persia and Arabia and finally, through Greece, they reached Europe. So far the Panchatantra has been translated into more than 50 languages of the world.

A unique feature of the tales is that most of the characters are animals; another is that the tales form a chain of stories; third, each of the tales has a distinct moral; and yet another, the tales have different levels of appeal.

The morals that the Panchatantra seeks to teach continue to be relevant to this day and the stories themselves have not lost their novelty even two thousand years after they were first told.

**Script: Kamala Chandrakant   Illustrations: Ram Waeerkar
Cover: Ram Waeerkar**

HOW THE JACKAL ATE THE ELEPHANT

MAHACHATURAKA, THE JACKAL WAS VERY HAPPY. HE HAD FOUND A DEAD ELEPHANT. ENOUGH FOOD FOR WEEKS!

BUT I'M GOING TO NEED HELP TO CUT INTO HIS HIDE AND REACH THE FLESH.

AT THAT MOMENT, A LION HAPPENED TO COME BY.

I'D BETTER OFFER HIM THE ELEPHANT AND WIN HIS FAVOUR.

1

MY LORD, YOUR HUMBLE SERVANT HAS BEEN GUARDING THIS DEAD ELEPHANT FOR YOU.

I EAT ONLY WHAT I HAVE KILLED.

DON'T I KNOW THAT!

I GIFT THIS ELEPHANT TO YOU, MY LOYAL SERVANT.

JUST AS I HAD EXPECTED.

BUT HOW AM I TO GET TO THE FLESH OF THE ELEPHANT?

AS HE WONDERED WHAT TO DO, A TIGER CAME BY.

OH! OH! I SENT OFF ONE FELLOW BY PRETENDING TO BE HUMBLE. HOW SHALL I SEND THIS ONE PACKING?

HE'S NOT ONE TO BE FLATTERED. I'LL HAVE TO THINK FAST.

CUNNING! THAT'S IT! I'LL RESORT TO CUNNING!

UNCLE! IT'S DANGEROUS FOR YOU TO BE HERE. THE LION WHO KILLED THIS ELEPHANT HAS GONE TO BATHE LEAVING ME HERE TO GUARD IT.

HE HATES TIGERS. ONE OF THEM ONCE ATE THE ELEPHANT HE HAD KILLED AND HE HAD TO EAT THE LEAVINGS.

HE HAS SWORN TO KILL EVERY TIGER HE MEETS IN THIS FOREST.

THANK YOU FOR WARNING ME, DEAR NEPHEW. DON'T TELL HIM YOU SAW ME. I'M OFF.

HA! HA! HA! HO! LOOK AT HIM RUN.

BUT I STILL HAVEN'T GOT TO THE FLESH OF THIS ELEPHANT!

JUST THEN, HE SAW A LEOPARD COMING TOWARDS HIM.

THAT'S THE FELLOW I'LL USE! HE HAS STRONG TEETH AND WILL CUT THROUGH THE HIDE IN NO TIME. THEN I'LL SEND HIM PACKING.

WELL, WELL, MY NEPHEW! YOU SEEM HUNGRY.

I AM. THAT'S A FINE ELEPHANT YOU HAVE THERE.

ISN'T IT? IT WAS KILLED BY A LION WHO LEFT ME HERE TO GUARD IT. BUT YOU MAY EAT SOME OF IT BEFORE HE GETS BACK, IF YOU'RE QUICK ENOUGH.

A LION, DID YOU SAY? NO! NO! THIS MEAT WOULD BE THE DEATH OF ME, IF I DON'T ESCAPE IN TIME!

COME ON. BE BOLD AND EAT. I'LL KEEP WATCH AND WARN YOU, IF I SEE HIM COMING.

THE LEOPARD NEEDED NO MORE COAXING. HE BEGAN TO TEAR AWAY AT THE ELEPHANT'S HIDE.

AS SOON AS THE HIDE WAS CUT THROUGH —

HERE COMES THE LION. QUICK! RUN OFF!

THE LEOPARD DID NOT EVEN STOP TO LOOK UP. TURNING ON HIS HEELS, HE RAN FOR HIS LIFE.

THE JACKAL WAS ABOUT TO FEED ON THE FLESH WHEN ANOTHER JACKAL CAME BY.

OH! THIS ONE IS MY EQUAL. I'LL FIGHT HIM OFF.

BARING HIS FANGS HE CHARGED...

...AND CHASED AWAY THE UNWELCOME GUEST.

ALL THIS MEAT! ALL FOR MYSELF! I NEED NOT LOOK FOR FOOD FOR WEEKS.

MORAL: MIGHTY BRAWN IS NO MATCH AGAINST NIMBLE BRAIN.

7

THE FROG KING AND THE SNAKE

GANGADATTA WAS THE KING OF THE FROGS WHO LIVED IN A WELL. HE COULD NOT GET ALONG WITH SOME OF HIS RELATIVES BECAUSE THEY OFTEN TREATED HIM BADLY.

ONE DAY HE TURNED TO HIS WIFE —

HOW DARE THEY TREAT ME, THEIR KING, IN THIS WAY! I MUST TEACH THEM A LESSON.

TAKE CARE, DEAR HUSBAND, THAT IN TRYING TO HARM THEM YOU DON'T GET US INTO TROUBLE.

BUT, IGNORING HER ADVICE, HE LEAPT FROM PAIL ...

...TO PAIL, UP THE WATER-WHEEL ...

...AND CAME OUT OF THE WELL. JUST THEN HE SAW PRIYADARSHANA, THE SNAKE, SLIDE INTO HIS HOLE.

AH! I'LL ASK HIM TO BE MY GUEST AND EAT MY WICKED RELATIVES.

HEY, PRIYA-DARSHANA! COME OUT.

THAT'S NO SNAKE CALLING ME. AND I DON'T HAVE ANY FRIENDS APART FROM SNAKES. PERHAPS IT'S A SNAKE CHARMER!

COME OUT, PRIYADARSHANA. I AM GANGADATTA, THE FROG-KING. I WANT TO MAKE FRIENDS WITH YOU.

IMPOSSIBLE! CAN HAY EVER MAKE FRIENDS WITH FIRE? WHAT YOU SAY MAKES NO SENSE.

I AGREE THAT WE ARE BORN ENEMIES. NEVERTHELESS, I NEED YOUR HELP. I WANT YOU TO EAT MY ENEMIES.

WHO ARE THESE ENEMIES?

MY OWN RELATIVES. THEY LIVE IN THE SAME WELL AS I DO.

OH! YOU LIVE IN A WELL! HOW AM I TO GET IN. AND EVEN IF I DID, WHERE WOULD I PERCH WHILE KILLING YOUR ENEMIES? GET AWAY WITH YOU!

WAIT, MY FRIEND, I'LL SHOW YOU HOW TO GET INTO THE WELL. AND I'LL ALSO SHOW YOU A COMFORTABLE HOLE, A LITTLE ABOVE THE WATER, W'HERE YOU CAN REST. PLEASE COME OUT.

THE SNAKE WAS DEEP IN THOUGHT FOR A WHILE.

I AM NO LONGER AS YOUNG AS I USED TO BE. ONCE IN A WHILE I CATCH A MOUSE AND THAT TOO WITH DIFFICULTY. HIS OFFER IS TEMPTING.

WELL, GANGADATTA, I HAVE DECIDED TO COME WITH YOU! LEAD AND I'LL FOLLOW.

THANK YOU, MY FRIEND. BUT THERE'S ONE THING. YOU MUST SPARE MY OWN FAMILY AND EAT ONLY THOSE WHOM I TELL YOU TO EAT.

YOU ARE MY FRIEND NOW, GANGA-DATTA. I WOULDN'T TOUCH YOUR FAMILY.

THE SNAKE THEN CAME OUT OF HIS HOLE.

COME. LET US NOT WASTE ANY TIME.

WHEN THEY REACHED THE EDGE OF THE WELL —

FOLLOW ME. IT'S VERY EASY.

A LITTLE LATER —

THAT'S THE HOLE. SETTLE YOURSELF THERE.

WHEN THE SNAKE WAS COMFORTABLY SETTLED —

THERE! THOSE ARE THE FROGS THAT TORMENT ME.

ONE BY ONE THE SNAKE SOON ATE UP ALL THE ENEMIES OF THE FROG-KING.

WHEN GANGADATTA IS NOT AROUND, I SHALL HELP MYSELF TO A FRIENDLY FROG OR TWO AS WELL.

WHEN GANGADATTA CAME TO SEE HIM —

I'VE EATEN ALL YOUR ENEMIES!

GOOD! NOW YOU MAY RETURN TO YOUR HOLE, THE WAY YOU CAME, MY FRIEND.

RETURN TO MY HOLE? YOU CAN'T BE SERIOUS. SOME OTHER SNAKE WOULD HAVE MOVED INTO IT THE VERY DAY I LEFT.

NO, MY FRIEND, I WILL HAVE TO STAY HERE. AND SINCE YOU TOOK ME OUT OF MY HOLE, IT IS YOUR DUTY TO FEED ME.

YOU MUST GIVE ME ONE FROG AT A TIME, FROM YOUR FRIENDS AND YOUR OWN FAMILY. IF YOU DON'T, I'LL EAT YOU ALL UP.

WHAT A FOOL I HAVE BEEN! WHY DID I EVER BRING HIM HERE? NOW I HAVE NO CHOICE BUT TO GIVE HIM A FROG EVERY DAY.

THE SNAKE HOWEVER NOT ONLY ATE THE FROG SENT TO HIM...

...BUT ANOTHER TOO BEHIND THE FROG-KING'S BACK.

ONE DAY, THE EXTRA FROG HE ATE WAS GANGADATTA'S OWN SON; AND GANGADATTA CAUGHT HIM IN THE ACT.

NO! NO! NOT THAT ONE, MY FRIEND. IT'S MY SON!

BUT IT WAS TOO LATE. ALL GANGADATTA'S WAILING COULD NOT BRING HIS SON BACK.

WHAT'S THE USE OF WAILING NOW? WHO IS THERE TO HELP YOU? YOU WANTED TO DESTROY YOUR OWN KIN! YOU'D BETTER ESCAPE FROM HERE OR THINK OF A PLOT TO KILL HIM.

THE DAYS WENT BY, GANGADATTA HAD NO PLAN AND ALL THE FROGS IN THE WELL WERE EATEN. ALL BUT HIMSELF.

DEAR GANGADATTA, I'M HUNGRY. PLEASE FIND ME SOMETHING TO EAT. IT'S YOUR DUTY TO DO SO.

THIS IS MY CHANCE TO ESCAPE.

MY FRIEND, AS LONG AS I'M ALIVE YOU WON'T GO HUNGRY. PERMIT ME TO LEAVE THIS WELL AND I'LL BRING YOU ALL THE FROGS FROM OTHER WELLS.

YOU, WHO HAVE BEEN LIKE A BROTHER TO ME, I'LL NEVER EAT NOW. IF YOU DO AS YOU PROMISE, YOU WILL BE LIKE A FATHER TO ME.

NOT WASTING ANOTHER MOMENT, THE FROG ESCAPED FROM THE WELL.

I'D BETTER FIND MYSELF ANOTHER WELL TO LIVE IN.

MEANWHILE, THE SNAKE WAITED IN VAIN FOR HIS RETURN.

I SHOULD NOT HAVE LET HIM GO.

14

MANY DAYS LATER, THE OLD SNAKE TURNED TO A LIZARD WHO LIVED IN THE SAME WELL.

MADAM, YOU AND GANGADATTA ARE OLD FRIENDS. PLEASE FIND HIM AND ASK HIM TO RETURN QUICKLY. NEVER MIND IF HE CAN'T GET OTHER FROGS TO COME.

TELL HIM THAT I WILL NOT HURT HIM; THAT I CAN'T LIVE WITHOUT HIM.

AFTER HUNTING IN ALL THE NEIGH-BOURING WELLS, THE LIZARD AT LAST FOUND THE FROG-KING.

DEAR GANGADATTA, WHAT ARE YOU DOING HERE? YOUR FRIEND, PRIYADARSHANA IS ANXIOUSLY AWAITING YOUR RETURN. HE PROMISES NOT TO HARM YOU. SO COME HOME.

A STARVING MAN IS NOT TO BE TRUSTED. I'VE LEARNT MY LESSON. HE WILL NEVER SEE ME AGAIN.

MORAL: DON'T CUT OFF YOUR NOSE TO SPITE YOUR FACE.

THE LION, THE JACKAL AND THE DONKEY

IN A JUNGLE THERE ONCE LIVED A LION WHO HAD A JACKAL FOR A SERVANT. WHENEVER THE LION KILLED AN ANIMAL, HE WOULD FIRST HAVE HIS FILL...

...AND LEAVE THE REST FOR THE JACKAL.

ONE DAY, THE LION MADE THE MISTAKE OF ATTACKING A FIERCE KING-ELEPHANT.

THE ELEPHANT WOUNDED HIM SO BADLY THAT HE COULD BARELY WALK.

FOR A WEEK, MASTER AND SERVANT STARVED. AT LAST, THE LION HAD AN IDEA.

IF YOU CAN BRING SOME ANIMAL TO ME WHICH I CAN KILL WITHOUT MUCH EFFORT, WE WON'T HAVE TO STARVE.

THE JACKAL SLOWLY ROSE TO HIS FEET AND SET OUT.

THAT'S A FINE DEER BUT TOO FAST FOR MY WOUNDED MASTER.

A FEW HOURS LATER —

AH! A DONKEY! JUST THE ANIMAL, I AM LOOKING FOR!

GOOD DAY UNCLE! WHY DO YOU LOOK SO FEEBLE?

HOW ELSE WOULD I LOOK, DEAR NEPHEW? I HAVE A CRUEL, MISERLY DHOBI FOR A MASTER. I AM OVERWORKED AND UNDERFED.

NOT A HANDFUL OF RICH FODDER HAVE I EATEN IN AGES! ALL THAT I LIVE ON IS THIS DRY GRASS.

IF THAT IS SO, WHY DON'T YOU COME AND LIVE WITH ME IN THE FOREST? THERE'S PLENTY OF RICH, GREEN GRASS NEAR MY CAVE.

IT IS VERY KIND OF YOU TO INVITE ME. BUT I AM A VILLAGE DWELLER. THE WILD ANIMALS OF THE JUNGLE WOULD SOON KILL ME.

YOU DON'T HAVE TO WORRY ABOUT THAT, UNCLE. NO ONE DARES TO COME NEAR MY CAVE. THEY FEAR MY POWERFUL PAWS AND CLAWS.

DO YOU KNOW, THREE SHE-DONKEYS WHO WERE TORTURED LIKE YOU BY THEIR MASTERS ARE NOW LIVING UNDER MY PROTECTION.

SHE-DONKEYS?

YES. THREE OF THEM! THEY HAVE GROWN PLUMP ON THE RICH, GREEN GRASS AND NOW WANT TO GET MARRIED. IN FACT, I HAVE COME IN SEARCH OF A HUSBAND FOR THEM. THAT'S WHY I WANT TO TAKE YOU BACK WITH ME.

LEAD ME TO THEM, DEAR NEPHEW. I TOO AM LOOKING FOR A BRIDE.

AND THE POOR DONKEY FOLLOWED THE JACKAL INTO THE JUNGLE.

FOOD AT LAST!

WHAT WAS THAT?

THE HASTY FOOL!

THE TERRIFIED DONKEY TOOK ONE LOOK AT THE LION...

...AND RAN FOR HIS LIFE.

A STUPID DONKEY AND YOU COULDN'T KILL HIM! O MASTER, HOW DID YOU DARE ATTACK AN ELEPHANT?

IT'S NOT MY FAULT. I WASN'T READY FOR HIM. I DIDN'T EXPECT YOU TO RETURN SO SOON.

THEN BE READY NOW. I'LL GO AND BRING HIM BACK.

BRING HIM BACK? IMPOSSIBLE! HE SAW ME AND RAN AWAY. YOU'LL HAVE TO BRING SOME OTHER ANIMAL.

I WILL BRING BACK THAT VERY DONKEY. BE READY FOR HIM THIS TIME.

WHEN THE JACKAL WENT BACK TO THE DONKEY—

SO YOU'RE BACK! A FINE SPOT YOU TOOK ME TO! IT'S MY LUCK THAT I ESCAPED FROM THAT HORRIBLE CREATURE!

THE JACKAL LAUGHED.

UNCLE, THAT WAS A LOVESICK SHE-DONKEY. WHEN SHE SAW YOU, SHE SPRANG FORWARD TO WELCOME YOU. BUT YOU WERE SHY AND RAN AWAY.

YOU MUST COME BACK AND MARRY HER. IF YOU DON'T, SHE SAYS SHE'LL STARVE HERSELF TO DEATH.

SHE CAN'T BEAR TO BE SEPARATED FROM YOU. SO HAVE MERCY ON HER AND RETURN. IF YOU DON'T, YOU WILL BE GUILTY OF KILLING A LADY AND KAMADEVA* WILL BE ANGRY WITH YOU.

BELIEVING ALL THAT THE JACKAL SAID, THE FOOLISH DONKEY WENT BACK WITH HIM TO THE JUNGLE.

WONDER OF WONDERS! HE HAS BROUGHT HIM BACK! THIS TIME I WON'T FAIL HIM.

WHEN THEY WERE NEAR ENOUGH—

DIDN'T I TELL YOU I WOULD SUCCEED IF I WERE READY? NOW GUARD THIS DONKEY WHILE I GO TO BATHE.

* GOD OF LOVE

21

I CANNOT WAIT TILL HE RETURNS. WHILE HE IS AWAY, I'LL EAT UP THE DONKEY'S HEART AND EARS.

WHEN THE LION RETURNED, HE BEGAN SNIFFING AT THE DONKEY. SUDDENLY, HE BEGAN TO ROAR.

YOU SCOUNDREL! YOU HAVE EATEN THE EARS AND HEART! AM I TO EAT YOUR LEAVINGS?

BUT THE JACKAL WAS NOT FRIGHTENED. CALMLY HE FACED THE LION.

O KING, THIS CREATURE WAS BORN WITHOUT EARS OR HEART. IF NOT, WOULD HE HAVE COME HERE, HEARD YOUR ROAR, RUN AWAY IN TERROR...

...AND THEN COME BACK AGAIN?

WHAT HE SAYS MUST BE TRUE. OR ELSE WHY SHOULD THE DONKEY HAVE COME BACK?

ALL RIGHT. I SHALL FIRST HAVE MY FILL OF THIS DONKEY. YOU MAY THEN EAT THE REST.

MORAL : DON'T LOSE YOUR HEAD IN THE FACE OF CALAMITIES AND YOU'LL OVERCOME THEM.

22

THE DHOBI'S* DONKEY

SHUDDHAPATA. THE DHOBI, LOVED HIS DONKEY BUT COULD NOT AFFORD TO FEED IT WELL.

ONE DAY, AS HE WAS RETURNING HOME THROUGH A THICK JUNGLE, THE DONKEY STUMBLED UNDER ITS LOAD, SO WEAK HAD IT BECOME.

MY POOR FEEBLE BEAST! IF ONLY I COULD GIVE YOU BETTER FODDER!

WHAT'S THAT?

OH! A DEAD TIGER! THANK GOD IT WASN'T A LIVE ONE!

* WASHERMAN

HE WAS ABOUT TO WALK ON, BUT SUDDENLY STOPPED.

THAT'S IT! I'LL FLAY THIS FELLOW AND TAKE THE SKIN HOME. MY DONKEY WILL NO LONGER LACK FOOD.

YOU WILL SOON BECOME A FEARFUL TIGER, MY GENTLE DONKEY, AND EAT ALL THE MILLET YOU WANT.

THERE! NOW, IN THIS GARB, GO INTO THE MILLET FIELDS AT NIGHT.

THAT NIGHT —

COME. IT'S TIME FOR YOU TO CHANGE.

THE DHOBI THEN LED HIM TO THE MILLET FIELDS.

GO, MY PET, AND EAT TO YOUR HEART'S CONTENT. I'LL COME BACK FOR YOU IN THE MORNING.

AN HOUR LATER, WHEN THE FARMER AND HIS MEN CAME TO MAKE THEIR USUAL ROUNDS—

THERE'S AN ANIMAL IN THE MILLET FIELD!

IT'S A TIGER! RUN!

AND THE DONKEY MUNCHED AWAY UNDISTURBED.

IN THE MORNING, THE DHOBI LED HIM HOME. THIS WENT ON FOR MANY DAYS.

YOU'VE GROWN SO PLUMP, MY DONKEY. IF YOU GROW ANY PLUMPER, YOU WILL NOT BE ABLE TO ENTER YOUR STALL.

ONE NIGHT—

THERE HE IS AGAIN!

WHAT SHALL WE DO? WE'RE HELPLESS.

JUST THEN, THE DONKEY HEARD THE BRAY OF A SHE-DONKEY.

EE-AW !

EE-AW

EE-AW EE-AW EE...

WE'VE BEEN DUPED. IT'S ONLY A DONKEY IN DISGUISE !

THE ANGRY FARMER AND HIS MEN CHARGED AT THE DONKEY AND BEAT HIM TO DEATH.

IN THE MORNING, THE DHOBI WAS SHOCKED TO SEE HIS DONKEY DEAD.

ALAS, MY FRIEND ! HOW DID IT HAPPEN ?

MORAL : SILENCE IS GOLDEN.

THE LIONESS AND THE JACKAL CUB

A LIONESS ONCE GAVE BIRTH TO TWO CUBS AND FOR A TIME COULD NOT GO OUT HUNTING.

SO HER HUSBAND WENT OUT...

...AND BROUGHT HOME THE GAME HE KILLED.

ONE DAY, HE COULD NOT FIND AN ANIMAL TO KILL. AS HE WAS RETURNING HOME —

WHAT'S THAT? A JACKAL CUB?

HE RAISED HIS PAW TO STRIKE IT WHEN PITY FOR THE TINY CREATURE OVERCAME HIM.

NO! HE'S JUST A CUB.

HOW CAN I KILL HIM?

PICKING THE CUB UP GENTLY WITH HIS TEETH...

...HE TOOK IT HOME ALIVE.

WHAT HAVE YOU BROUGHT TODAY?

I COULDN'T FIND A SINGLE ANIMAL. THEN I SAW THIS CUB. I DIDN'T HAVE THE HEART TO KILL HIM.

BUT YOU MAY KILL AND EAT HIM IF YOU LIKE.

WHEN YOU DIDN'T HAVE THE HEART TO KILL HIM, HOW CAN I?

HE SHALL GROW UP AS MY THIRD SON.

THE THREE CUBS SOON GREW PLUMP AND FRISKY.

ONE DAY —

WHO IS THAT INTRUDER? COME, BROTHERS, LET'S GO AND ATTACK HIM.

WAIT, BROTHERS. DON'T! THAT'S AN ELEPHANT. AN ENEMY OF OUR RACE. LET'S RUN AWAY!

RUN AWAY? HA! HA!

WHAT'S SO FUNNY? I'M GOING TO RUN AWAY. LET THEM FOLLOW IF THEY WANT TO.

LATER AT THE DEN —

...AND, MOTHER, IT WAS SO FUNNY! HO! HO! THE WAY HE PUT HIS TAIL BETWEEN HIS LEGS. HA! HA!...

HO! HO... AND RAN FOR HIS LIFE... HA! HA!

YOU ARE FOOLS. I SHOULD HAVE LET THAT ELEPHANT KILL YOU. I WISH I HADN'T WARNED YOU. I...

CALM DOWN, MY SON. LET US GO OUTSIDE. I WANT TO TALK TO YOU.

WHEN THEY WERE ALONE —

YOU MUST NEVER AGAIN SPEAK LIKE THAT TO THEM. THEY ARE YOUR OLDER BROTHERS.

SO WHAT? DO YOU THINK I AM INFERIOR TO THEM IN ANY WAY? WHY DO THEY MAKE FUN OF ME? I'M GOING TO KILL THEM!

THE LIONESS HELD BACK THE SMILE THAT CAME TO HER LIPS.

POOR CUB. I WILL HAVE TO TELL HIM THE TRUTH— BEFORE IT'S TOO LATE.

MY CUB, YOU ARE THE SON OF A JACKAL. I BROUGHT YOU UP BECAUSE YOU WERE HELPLESS.

AS LONG AS MY SONS ARE CUBS, THEY WILL NOT HARM YOU. RUN AWAY AND JOIN YOUR OWN PACK BEFORE THEY KNOW YOU TO BE A JACKAL.

IF YOU DON'T, MY SONS WILL SOONER OR LATER FIGHT YOU AND KILL YOU.

THE POOR JACKAL WAS SO TERRIFIED WHEN HE HEARD THIS, THAT WITHOUT A WORD HE SLUNK AWAY TO FIND HIS OWN PACK.

MORAL: YOU ARE BEST OFF WITH YOUR OWN KIND.

Inspiring Tales from
Amar Chitra Katha

Biographies in the Amar Chitra Katha series

Vivekananda
Swami Chinmayananda
Ashoka
Rani of Jhansi
Subhash Chandra Bose
Babasaheb Ambedkar

Lokmanya Tilak
Mahatma Gandhi
Jawaharlal Nehru
Jayaprakash Narayan
Kalpana Chawla
Rani Durgavati

Bhagat Singh
J.R.D. Tata
Guru Gobind Singh
Rabindranath Tagore
Lal Bahadur Shastri
Veer Savarkar

These 32-page comic books are now available at a special online price of
Rs 25 (MRP Rs 30) at www.AmarChitraKatha.com. Start your collection today!

INDIA BOOK HOUSE

Mahalaxmi Chambers, 5th Floor, 22 Bhulabhai Desai Road, Mumbai 400 026, India
Tel 23523827 Fax 23538406 Email info@amarchitrakatha.com

AMAR CHITRA KATHA

Panchatantra
The Dullard and other Stories

Illustrated Classics From India

Panchatantra
The Dullard and Other Stories

Panchatantra is the oldest collection of stories for children, written originally by Pandit Vishnu Sharma. One of the versions by Vasubhaga Bhatta is now lost. However, fortunately the stories in Bhatta's edition can be found in the Kannada translation by Durgasimha, a minister in the Chalukyan kingdom of Jayasimha. It contains twenty stories that are not usually included in the popular editions of Panchatantra.

This Amar Chitra Katha is based on stories from Durgasimha's Panchatantra.

Script: Kamala Chandrakant   Illustrations: Pradeep Sathe
Cover: Pradeep Sathe

THE DULLARD

THERE WERE ONCE FOUR BRAHMANS WHO HAD GROWN UP TOGETHER IN THE SAME VILLAGE. THREE OF THEM SPENT ALL THEIR TIME PORING OVER SCHOLARLY TEXTS, BUT NOT SO THE FOURTH.

ONE DAY—

WHY DON'T WE TRAVEL TO THE CITY? WE COULD MAKE USE OF OUR LEARNING AND COLLECT A FORTUNE.

NOT A BAD IDEA. BUT WE'RE NOT TAKING THAT DULLARD WITH US. HE'D ONLY BE A BURDEN.

YOU'RE RIGHT. HE DOESN'T KNOW A THING!

HOW COULD YOU BE SO UNKIND! HE'S GROWN UP WITH US. WE CAN'T LEAVE HIM BEHIND. HE'LL SHARE WHAT WE MAKE.

OH! ALL RIGHT! LET HIM COME.

AND SO THE FOUR SET OUT.

AS THEY PASSED THROUGH A FOREST—

OH GOD! THESE SEEM TO BE THE BONES OF A LION!

WHY DON'T WE TEST OUR LEARNING ON THESE BONES? I CAN PUT THE BONES TOGETHER AND MAKE A SKELETON.

I CAN GIVE THE SKELETON MUSCLE AND SKIN.

WELL IF YOU DO THAT, I CAN BREATHE LIFE INTO IT.

2

GOOD LORD, MY GUESS WAS RIGHT! IT IS THE SKELETON OF A LION.

THAT WAS REALLY CLEVER OF YOU.

YOU ARE A SCHOLAR, INDEED!

NOW IT'S MY TURN. WATCH THIS!

DO YOU SEE THAT? NOW DON'T YOU WISH YOU TOO HAD LEARNT ALL THIS? AREN'T YOU EAGER TO SEE IT COME ALIVE?

NO! NO! I'M NOT! IT'S A LION. IF IT COMES ALIVE IT WILL KILL US ALL! PLEASE DON'T...

BE QUIET, YOU UNGRATEFUL FELLOW. IT WAS I WHO COAXED THE OTHERS TO LET YOU COME ALONG. AND NOW YOU WANT TO DENY ME THE CHANCE TO TEST AND PROVE MY SCHOLARSHIP!

IGNORE HIM. WHAT DOES HE UNDERSTAND OF THESE THINGS?

ALL RIGHT. DO AS YOU WISH. BUT LET IT NOT BE SAID THAT I DIDN'T...

...WARN YOU!

MY POOR LEARNED FRIENDS! IF ONLY YOU HAD HEEDED WHAT MY COMMON-SENSE TOLD ME.

MORAL: MERE SCHOLARSHIP WITHOUT COMMON SENSE IS FUTILE.

4

THE GREEDY BARBER

MANIBHADRA THE MERCHANT WAS VIRTUOUS, RICH AND GENEROUS.

MEN FLOCKED TO HIS HOME TO ENJOY HIS HOSPITALITY.

THEN ONE DAY, BY MAKING A BAD INVESTMENT HE LOST ALL HIS WEALTH; AND CONSEQUENTLY HIS FRIENDS.

HOW CAN I BLAME THEM? EVEN IF THEY DID COME IN, WHAT COULD I OFFER THEM?

MY KINDNESS? MY NOBILITY? MY LOVE? WHAT ARE THEY WORTH? NOTHING!

WITHOUT MONEY, I AM WORTH NOTHING. WHY SHOULD I LIVE? I'LL... STARVE MYSELF... TO DEATH.

AS THE MERCHANT FELL ASLEEP HE HAD AN AMAZING DREAM.

A GOOD MAN LIKE YOU MUST LIVE. I WILL COME TO YOUR DOOR TOMORROW IN THIS FORM.

TOUCH ME ON MY HEAD WITH A STICK AND I'LL TURN INTO GOLD; MORE GOLD THAN YOU COULD USE IN THIS LIFETIME.

THE NEXT MORNING—

WHAT A DREAM THAT WAS! WILL IT COME TRUE?

OF COURSE, NOT. IT WON'T. IT'S BECAUSE I WORRY DAY AND NIGHT ABOUT MONEY THAT I DREAMT ABOUT IT TOO.

SOMEONE'S KNOCKING AT THE DOOR!

KNOCK KNOCK

I'LL OPEN IT. IT MUST BE THE BARBER.

IT WAS THE BARBER. AS HE GOT DOWN TO WORK —

JUST A MINUTE. THERE'S ANOTHER KNOCK AT THE DOOR.

KNOCK KNOCK

IMPOSSIBLE! IT'S THE VERY MONK I SAW IN MY DREAM.

COME IN, SIR. DO COME IN.

IF THE REST OF THE DREAM COMES TRUE, I'LL SOON BE A RICH MAN AGAIN.

I CAN'T BELIEVE IT!

I'LL GIVE THE FELLOW SOME. LET HIM SHARE OUR GOOD FORTUNE.

THANK GOD! OUR BAD DAYS HAVE COME TO AN END.

THAT'S FOR YOU. AND DON'T TELL A SOUL ABOUT WHAT YOU JUST SAW.

I WON'T! YOU CAN TRUST ME.

SO THESE MONKS TURN INTO GOLD WHEN THEY ARE CLOUTED!

THE NEXT MORNING—

THERE! THIS SHOULD BE GOOD ENOUGH!

NOW TO THE MONASTERY.

TOWARDS NOON —

HOLY SIRS, I HAVE SOME EXCELLENT CANVAS STRIPS TO WRAP MANUSCRIPTS IN. AND SOME MONEY FOR MONKS WHO ARE ENGAGED IN PIOUS WORKS.

PERHAPS YOU COULD USE THE MONEY AND THE CANVAS.

WE CERTAINLY COULD, GENEROUS ONE.

THEN PLEASE COME WITH ME.

AS SOON AS THEY REACHED THE BARBER'S HOUSE —

WHERE IS THE CANVAS?

I'LL FIRST HAVE TO MAKE THE MONEY TO BUY IT WITH! AND YOU WILL HELP ME DO IT!

9

HELP!

AA-AH!

I'D BETTER RUN FOR MY LIFE.

HELP! THE FELLOW HAS GONE MAD!

HE'S A MURDERER!

THEIR CRIES CAUGHT THE ATTENTION OF THE CITY GUARDS.

WHAT'S THE MATTER?

A LUNATIC! IN THERE!

HE'S A MURDERER! THERE ARE OTHERS IN THERE! SAVE THEM!

HELP!

AA-AH!

SPARE ME!

WHAT A WASTE OF ENERGY! NOT ONE OF THEM HAS TURNED INTO ··· HEY!

LET ME GO. TAKE YOUR HANDS OFF ME! WHAT'S ALL THIS?

WE'D LIKE TO KNOW. SO WOULD THE CITY JUDGE.

LATER—

WHAT HARM HAD THOSE POOR MONKS DONE YOU, YOU WICKED FELLOW?

NOTHING, SIR. BUT HOW ELSE COULD I GET RICH?

AND HE DESCRIBED WHAT HE HAD SEEN AT MANIBHADRA'S HOUSE.

SUMMON THE MERCHANT TO COURT.

WHEN MANIBHADRA CAME —

THIS BARBER SAYS HE SAW YOU HITTING A MONK. DID YOU?

WELL, I DIDN'T HIT HIM. BUT IT MIGHT HAVE APPEARED SO TO ONE WHO DIDN'T KNOW THE WHOLE STORY!

MANIBHADRA THEN TOLD THE JUDGE ALL ABOUT HIMSELF, HIS DREAM AND THE MONK'S COMMAND.

SO THAT'S WHY MY MONKS DIDN'T TURN INTO GOLD! WHAT A FOOL I HAVE BEEN!

NOT JUST A FOOL BUT A GREEDY FOOL! YOU SHALL PAY FOR YOUR CRIME BY GOING TO PRISON!

MORAL: BLIND IMITATION IS A DANGEROUS THING.

11

THE MONGOOSE AND THE BRAHMAN'S WIFE

A KIND BRAHMAN ONCE FOUND A BABY MONGOOSE WHINING NEAR ITS DEAD MOTHER.

YOU POOR THING. I'LL TAKE YOU HOME WITH ME.

MY DEAR, YOU'LL HAVE TO BRING UP THIS LITTLE BABY, TOO.

WHY NOT! I LOVE LITTLE ONES. BRING HIM HERE.

THE WEE, HELPLESS MONGOOSE...

...SOON GREW INTO A PLUMP, STRONG CREATURE WITH SHARP TEETH.

MUCH AS I LOVE HIM, HE IS AFTER ALL A WILD ANIMAL.

I'LL HAVE TO BE CAREFUL.

I'M OFF TO THE RIVER. SEE THAT THE MONGOOSE DOES NOT HURT OUR SON.

HOW CAN HE HURT HIS OWN BROTHER? YOU WORRY UNNECESSARILY.

A LITTLE LATER—

IT'S TIME TO GO BEGGING FOR ALMS. I'D BETTER LEAVE.

AS THE BRAHMAN LEFT—

A SNAKE! HE'S OUT TO GET MY BROTHER!

AR-R-R! NO YOU DON'T! NOT WHEN I'M AROUND.

THERE! I'VE FINISHED HIM. I MUST LET MOTHER KNOW THAT MY BROTHER IS SAFE!

AH! THERE SHE IS! HOW PROUD SHE'LL BE WHEN SHE LEARNS OF MY BRAVERY.

14

BLOOD! YOU BRUTE! YOU'VE KILLED MY SON!

TAKE THAT, YOU UNGRATEFUL BEAST!

MY POOR BABY! WHY DID I EVER AGREE TO...

...A SNAKE! THE MONGOOSE... BLOOD... NO!

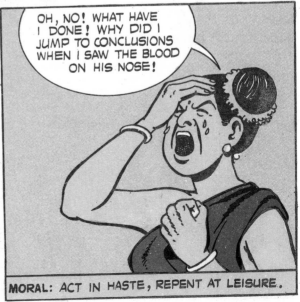

OH, NO! WHAT HAVE I DONE! WHY DID I JUMP TO CONCLUSIONS WHEN I SAW THE BLOOD ON HIS NOSE!

MORAL: ACT IN HASTE, REPENT AT LEISURE.

THE WHEEL-BEARER

FOUR FRIENDS ONCE MADE THEIR WAY . . .

. . . TO THE REMOTE HERMITAGE OF YOGI BHAIRAVANANDA.

WHY HAVE YOU COME HERE?

WE SEEK YOUR HELP AND GUIDANCE. WE KNOW THAT YOU ARE GIFTED WITH STRANGE POWERS.

WE HAVE COME OUT OF OUR HOMES TO FIND SOME GOLD OR DIE IN THE ATTEMPT.

WE ARE CERTAIN THAT WHAT FOOLS CALL FATE OR LUCK IS ONLY THE FRUIT OF SINCERE EFFORT.

THEY SEEM TO BE COURAGEOUS AND DETERMINED. THEY SHOULD MAKE GOOD DISCIPLES.

I THINK I'LL HELP THEM. I HOPE THEY DON'T HAVE TO REGRET IT!

HE WENT INTO HIS HUT AND CAME OUT WITH FOUR COTTON WICKS.

I'LL GIVE EACH OF YOU ONE OF THESE WICKS.

TAKE THEM AND WALK TO THE MOUNTAINS. THE MOMENT A WICK FALLS, DIG THE GROUND AND YOU'LL FIND SOME TREASURE. COLLECT IT AND GO HOME.

THE FOUR FRIENDS BOUGHT SOME PICKAXES AND SET OUT.

WHATEVER WE FIND, WE'LL SHARE EQUALLY AMONG US.

AS THEY NEARED THE SLOPES OF THE MOUNTAINS —

HEY! THE WICK SLIPPED OUT OF MY HAND!

QUICK! LET'S DIG UP THE TREASURE.

KEEPING THE WICKS IN THEIR SLING-BAGS, THE OTHER THREE HELPED HIM.

LOOK! COPPER ORE! COME ALL OF YOU. LET'S CARRY AS MUCH AS WE CAN AND GO HOME.

HOW MUCH CAN IT FETCH US?

FOOL! IT'S ONLY COPPER.

LET'S GO FARTHER.

YOU MAY GO FARTHER IF YOU LIKE. I'M CONTENT WITH THIS. I'M RETURNING HOME.

A FEW DAYS LATER WHEN THE SECOND WICK FELL —

IT'S SILVER! WHY GO ANY FARTHER? LET'S TAKE WHAT WE CAN AND RETURN HOME.

AND NOT SEE WHAT WE MIGHT FIND AHEAD? IT MIGHT BE WHAT WE CAME OUT FOR— GOLD!

GOLD! LET'S GO!

YOU MAY DO AS YOU PLEASE. I'M GOING HOME.

THE TWO FRIENDS TRUDGED ON TILL THE THIRD WICK FELL.

GOLD! WE'VE GOT WHAT WE SET OUT TO GET. WE NEEDN'T GO ANY FARTHER.

BUT WE STILL HAVE ONE WICK LEFT. IT'S BOUND TO BRING US PRECIOUS GEMS. A HANDFUL OF WHICH WOULD FETCH US MORE THAN ALL THIS GOLD WOULD. COME. FOLLOW ME.

I'LL TELL YOU WHAT. YOU GO AHEAD. I'LL WAIT HERE FOR YOU.

SO THE FOURTH FRIEND WALKED ON, ALONE.

IT'S A HOT DAY INDEED! THE SUN IS MERCILESS. BUT I MUST NOT GIVE UP.

OH, WHAT I WOULDN'T GIVE FOR A DROP OF WATER! RIGHT NOW IT SEEMS MORE PRECIOUS TO ME THAN THE MOST PRECIOUS OF GEMS.

HE WALKED ON AND ON BUT THE WICK REFUSED TO FALL.

I SEEM TO HAVE LOST MY WAY! WHATEVER I DO, I SEEM TO BE WALKING IN CIRCLES. WHERE AM I?

AA-A-AH!

20

WHAT ARE YOU DOING HERE WITH THAT WHEEL ON YOUR HEAD? ANYWAY CAN YOU TELL ME WHERE I COULD GET SOME WATER?

I'M DYING OF THIRST. OH, IF ONLY I COULD BE RELIEVED OF THIS THIRST FOREVER!

WH — WHAT'S THE MEANING OF THIS? KEEP THAT WHEEL AWAY!

I CAN'T, GOOD SIR. IT'S THE WORK OF THE GOD OF WEALTH — TO PROTECT HIS TREASURES FROM SEEKERS LIKE US. YOU WILL NOW BE FREE FROM HUNGER, THIRST, OLD AGE AND DEATH.

BUT HOW... WHEN DO I BECOME FREE OF THIS TORTURE?

WHEN ANOTHER SEEKER CARRYING ONE OF THOSE WICKS COMES AND SPEAKS TO YOU.

OOO—H! AA—AH! I CAN'T BEAR THE PAIN! OO—OH! MY HEAD! HOW LONG HAVE YOU BEEN HERE?

I DON'T KNOW. BUT I SET OUT, WITH A MAGIC WICK, WHEN RAMA WAS KING OF AYODHYA. GREEDY FOR SOMETHING MORE THAN COPPER, SILVER OR GOLD, I REACHED THIS PLACE IN SEARCH OF GEMS.

I SAW A MAN WITH A WHEEL ON HIS HEAD AND... I DON'T HAVE TO TELL YOU THE REST. I AM GRATEFUL TO YOU FOR SETTING ME FREE. FAREWELL.

MEANWHILE—

WHY HASN'T MY FRIEND RETURNED AS YET? I'D BETTER FOLLOW HIS FOOTPRINTS AND GO IN SEARCH OF HIM. HE MIGHT BE IN TROUBLE.

A FEW HOURS LATER —

AH! THERE YOU ARE! BUT WHAT ARE YOU DOING TO YOURSELF? THROW OFF THAT WHEEL AT ONCE AND COME AWAY WITH ME.

OOO—OH! I CAN'T... A QUIRK OF FATE... IT WAS LIKE THIS...

WHEN HE FINISHED HIS STRANGE TALE—

WHAT YOU CALL A QUIRK OF FATE WAS YOUR OWN GREED. WE SET OUT TO FIND GOLD AND WE FOUND IT.

BUT YOU WERE NOT CONTENT. YOU WANTED GEMS. NOW YOU WILL HAVE TO STAY HERE AND PAY FOR YOUR GREED.

MY POOR FRIEND! MUCH AS I HATE TO LEAVE HIM IN THIS PLIGHT, I HAVE NO CHOICE. I AM POWER-LESS TO HELP HIM!

MORAL: BE AMBITIOUS, BUT NOT AVARICIOUS.

EKABUDDHI

TWO FISH NAMED SHATABUDDHI AND SAHASRABUDDHI, A FROG NAMED EKABUDDHI AND HIS WIFE, ALL LIVED TOGETHER IN A SHALLOW POND.

ONE EVENING, TWO FISHERMEN HAPPENED TO PASS BY THE POND.

LOOK! LOOK AT THOSE BEAUTIES! LET'S GET TO WORK AND CATCH THEM.

NOT NOW. IT'S GETTING DARK. WE'LL COME BACK IN THE MORNING.

DID YOU HEAR THAT? WE'D BETTER FLEE FROM HERE.

CERTAINLY NOT. WE'LL STAY ON. ANYTHING CAN HAPPEN. THEY MIGHT NOT COME TOMORROW.

SUPPOSE THEY DO COME?

IF THEY DO, I KNOW A THOUSAND TRICKS BY WHICH I CAN SAVE ALL FOUR OF US.

NO, EKABUDDHI, WE SHOULD NOT ABANDON OUR HOME FOR FEAR OF THE WORDS OF SOME FISHERMEN.

YOU ARE RIGHT, SAHASRABUDDHI. BESIDES I KNOW ANOTHER HUNDRED TRICKS IF YOUR ONE THOUSAND FAIL!

THE ONLY TRICK I KNOW IS TO FORESEE DANGER AND ACT ACCORDINGLY.

I AM OFF WITH MY WIFE TO A SAFER PLACE I KNOW.

THE NEXT MORNING —

25

OH! OH! THIS NET IS IMPOSSIBLE! IF ONLY I COULD GET OUT, I WOULD BE ABLE TO DO SOMETHING.

WE'RE TRAPPED! WE'RE FINISHED.

PUT THIS LOT INTO THE BASKET. WE'LL SELL THE TWO BIG FELLOWS SEPARATELY.

THEY SHOULD FETCH US A GOOD PRICE.

AS THE FISHERMEN WALKED AWAY—

BUT FOR MY CAUTIOUS NATURE WE TOO WOULD HAVE BEEN IN THAT BASKET.

MORAL: PREVENTION IS BETTER THAN CURE.

THE LAZY BRAHMAN

THERE WAS ONCE A LAZY BRAHMAN WHO LIVED SOLELY ON THE ALMS THAT HE COLLECTED. ONE DAY A KIND HOUSEWIFE GAVE HIM MORE FLOUR THAN HE NEEDED.

WHAT A STROKE OF LUCK! NOW I CAN GO RIGHT BACK HOME TO MY CHARPOY.

I'LL USE A LITTLE OF IT AND SAVE THE REST.

THERE! THAT SHOULD KEEP IT SAFE FROM THE RATS.

IF I SAVE THAT FLOUR TILL THERE IS A FAMINE IN THE LAND, I SHOULD GET QUITE SOME MONEY FOR IT.

"WITH THAT MONEY I'LL BUY A HE-GOAT AND A SHE-GOAT."

"SOON I'LL HAVE A FLOCK OF GOATS."

" I'LL SELL THOSE AND BUY A BULL AND A COW."

" WHEN THEY HAVE MULTIPLIED INTO A LARGE HERD..."

"...I'LL SELL THEM AND BUY MYSELF A PAIR OF BUFFALOES."

" WHEN THEY BREED, I'LL SELL THE LOT AND BUY A PAIR OF HORSES."

"SOON I'LL HAVE MANY HORSES. AND WITH ALL THE MONEY THEY'LL FETCH, I'LL BUY MYSELF A MANSION."

"SOME FATHER WILL OFFER HIS LOVELY DAUGHTER TO ME IN MARRIAGE."

"A SON WILL BE BORN TO US AND I'LL CALL HIM SOMA SHARMA.

"SOON HE'LL BEGIN TO CRAWL."

"I'LL BE WORRIED THAT THE HORSES WILL TRAMPLE HIM."

29

"I'LL SCREAM TO HIS MOTHER TO TAKE HIM AWAY INSIDE. BUT SHE'LL BE SO BUSY SHE WON'T HEAR ME.

MORAL: DON'T COUNT YOUR CHICKENS BEFORE THEY ARE HATCHED.

Classic Collections

The immortal tales of Amar Chitra Katha
are now available as 3-in-I digests with a special
selection of three delightful tales in one comic book.

Tales from the Panchatantra
Tales of Birbal
More Tales of Birbal
Great Plays of Kalidasa
Great Sanskrit Plays
Great Indian Emperors
Vishnu the Saviour
Ranas of Mewar

Matchless Wits
More Tales from the Jatakas
Vishnu to the Rescue
Buddhist Tales
More Buddhist Tales
Tales told by Sri Ramakrishna
Further Tales from the Jatakas
The Sons of the Pandavas

Each 96-page digest is now available at a special online price of
Rs 68 (MRP Rs 80) at www.AmarChitraKatha.com. Start your collection today!

INDIA BOOK HOUSE

Mahalaxmi Chambers, 5th Floor, 22 Bhulabhai Desai Road, Mumbai 400 026, India.
Tel.: 2352 3409, 2352 5636 Fax: 2353 8406 E-mail: info@amarchitrakath.com

Timeless Treasures

The legendary sagas of Amar Chitra Katha are now
available as 5-in-1 digests with a distinctive compilation
of five enthralling tales in one comic book.

Stories of Birbal

Great Rulers of India

Stories from the Jatakas

Brave Rajputs

Stories from the Panchatantra

Ancient Tales of Wit and Wisdom

Stories of Rama

Further Stories from the Jatakas

More Stories from the Jatakas

Stories from the Bhagawat

Devotees of Vishnu

Stories of Buddha

Heroes from the Mahabharata

Stories from the Mahabharata

Stories from Sanskrit Drama

Great Freedom Fighters

**Each 160-page digest is now available at a special online price of
Rs 175 (MRP Rs 195) at www.AmarChitraKatha.com. Start your collection today!**

INDIA BOOK HOUSE

Mahalaxmi Chambers, 5th Floor, 22 Bhulabhai Desai Road, Mumbai 400 026, India.
Tel.: 2352 3409, 2352 5636 Fax: 2353 8406 E-mail: info@amarchitrakath.com